Graded examples  **cs**

Geometry and Trigonometry

M. R. Heylings M.A., M.Sc.

Schofield & Sims Limited   Huddersfield

0 7217 2331 4

First printed 1984
Reprinted 1985
Reprinted 1986
Reprinted 1987

The series **Graded examples in mathematics**
comprises:

Fractions and Decimals	0 7217 2323 3
Answer Book	0 7217 2324 1
Algebra	0 7217 2325 x
Answer Book	0 7217 2326 8
Area and Volume	0 7217 2327 6
Answer Book	0 7217 2328 4
General Arithmetic	0 7217 2329 2
Answer Book	0 7217 2330 6
Geometry and Trigonometry	0 7217 2331 4
Answer Book	0 7217 2332 2
Negative Numbers and Graphs	0 7217 2333 0
Answer Book	0 7217 2334 9
Matrices and Transformations	0 7217 2335 7
Answer Book	0 7217 2336 5
Sets, Probability and Statistics	0 7217 2337 3
Answer Book	0 7217 2338 1
Revision of Topics for GCSE	0 7217 2339 x
Answer Book	0 7217 2340 3

Designed by Graphic Art Concepts, Leeds
Printed in England by Pindar Print Limited, Scarborough, North Yorkshire

Author's Note

This series has been written and produced in the form of eight topic books, each offering a wealth of graded examples for pupils in the 11-16 age range; plus a further book of revision examples for those nearing examination in year 5.

There are no teaching points in the series. The intention is to meet the often heard request from teachers for a wide choice of graded examples to support their own class teaching. The contents are clearly labelled for easy use in conjunction with an existing course book; but the books can also be used as the chief source of examples, in which case the restrictions imposed by the traditional type of mathematics course book are removed and the teacher is free to organise year-by-year courses to suit the school. Used in this way, the topic-book approach offers an unusual and useful continuity of work for the class-room, for homework or for revision purposes.

The material has been tested over many years in classes ranging from mixed ability 11-year-olds to fifth formers taking public examinations. Some sections are useful for pupils of above average ability while other sections suit the needs of the less able, though it is for the middle range of ability that the series is primarily intended.

"Graded examples in mathematics" and the GCSE

The advent of GCSE has increased the demands made on the teaching and learning of mathematics. A heavy stress is laid on the content of a mathematics programme being related to applications and contexts, particularly those from everyday situations, and being such that pupils increase their self-confidence by experiencing success in their work. The exercises offered in this series are so graded as to encourage success; in addition, throughout the series, a continuing emphasis is placed on providing exercises where pupils can apply the topic being studied in a variety of contexts and situations. The series thus offers a highly flexible and motivating preparation for GCSE.

Contents

Geometry

Trigonometry

Further topics

Symbols

$=$	is equal to
$\neq$	is not equal to
$\simeq$	is approximately equal to
$<$	is less than
$\leqslant$	is less than or equal to
$\not<$	is not less than
$>$	is greater than
$\geqslant$	is greater than or equal to
$\not>$	is not greater than
$\Rightarrow$	implies
$\Leftarrow$	is implied by
$\rightarrow$	maps onto
$\in$	is a member of
$\notin$	is not a member of
$\subset$	is a subset of
$\not\subset$	is not a subset of
$\cap$	intersection (or overlap)
$\cup$	union
A'	the complement (or outside) of set A
$\mathscr{E}$	The Universal set
$\varnothing$ or $\{\ \}$	the empty set
(x, y)	the co-ordinates of a point
$\begin{pmatrix} x \\ y \end{pmatrix}$	the components of a vector

The Greek alphabet

A	α	alpha
B	β	beta
Γ	γ	gamma
Δ	δ	delta
E	ε	epsilon
Z	ζ	zeta
H	η	eta
Θ	θ	theta
I	ι	iota
K	κ	kappa
Λ	λ	lambda
M	μ	mu
N	ν	nu
Ξ	ξ	xi
O	o	omicron
Π	π	pi
P	ρ	rho
Σ	σ, ς	sigma
T	τ	tau
Y	υ	upsilon
Φ	ϕ, φ	phi
X	χ	chi
Ψ	ψ	psi
Ω	ω	omega

Geometry

Turns and degrees

1 How many full turns does the big (minute) hand of a clock go through in

    a 1 hour   b 2 hours   c 4 hours

    d 6 hours   e 12 hours   f $\frac{1}{2}$ hour

    g 30 min   h 15 min   i 1 day?

2 What direction am I facing if I start by facing

    a north and rotate a $\frac{1}{2}$ turn

    b north and rotate a $\frac{1}{4}$ turn clockwise

    c north and rotate a $\frac{1}{4}$ turn anticlockwise

    d east and rotate a $\frac{1}{2}$ turn

    e east and rotate a $\frac{1}{4}$ turn clockwise

    f east and rotate a $\frac{1}{4}$ turn anticlockwise

    g south and rotate a $\frac{1}{2}$ turn

    h south and rotate a $\frac{1}{4}$ turn clockwise

    i west and rotate a $\frac{1}{2}$ turn

    j west and rotate a $\frac{3}{4}$ turn clockwise?

3 The numbered list gives ten actions which involve turning. The lettered list gives the number of turns which are made.

Pair each letter from **A** to **J** with a number from **1** to **10**.

1	Turning a door handle	**A**	3 turns
2	A clock's minute hand moving for three hours	**B**	$1\frac{1}{2}$ turns
3	Removing the cap on a tube of toothpaste	**C**	$\frac{1}{4}$ turn
4	Playing a single record	**D**	120 turns
5	A soldier doing an 'about-turn'	**E**	600 turns
6	A clock's hour hand moving for nine hours	**F**	$\frac{1}{2}$ turn
7	A screw being screwed into a piece of wood	**G**	$\frac{3}{4}$ turn
8	An athlete running eight laps of a track	**H**	$\frac{1}{52}$ turn
9	Playing an LP record	**I**	8 turns
10	The Earth rotating about the Sun for one week	**J**	15 turns

4 Which of these six angles are $\frac{1}{4}$ turns?

Turns and degrees

5   Match these five fractions with the five angles shown.
Write the letter of each angle with its corresponding fraction.

$\frac{1}{2}$ turn $\frac{1}{4}$ turn $\frac{1}{8}$ turn $\frac{3}{4}$ turn $\frac{3}{8}$ turn

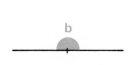   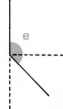

6   Write the seven angles (**a** to **g**) in order of size, with the *smallest* first.

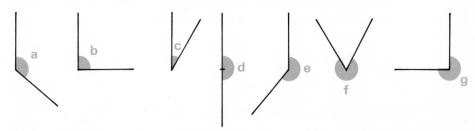

7   a   How many times does the Earth go round the Sun in one year?

b   What fraction of a full turn does it rotate through between December and June?

c   What fraction of a full turn does it rotate through between December and March?

d   What fraction of a full turn does it rotate through in one day?

e   How many days did the Ancient Babylonians think there were in one year?

f   What name do we give to $\frac{1}{360}$ of a full turn?

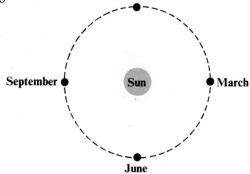

8   How many degrees are there in

a   one full turn   b   a half turn

c   a quarter turn   d $\frac{3}{4}$ of a turn

e   two full turns   f $1\frac{1}{2}$ full turns

g $\frac{1}{360}$ of a turn?

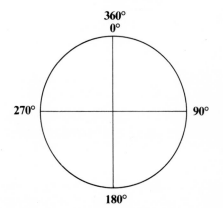

Turns and degrees

9 How many degrees are there in

a $\frac{1}{2}$ turn   b $\frac{1}{4}$ turn   c $\frac{1}{8}$ turn   d $\frac{1}{10}$ turn

e $\frac{1}{6}$ turn   f $\frac{1}{12}$ turn   g $\frac{1}{3}$ turn   h $\frac{1}{5}$ turn

i $\frac{1}{9}$ turn   j $\frac{1}{20}$ turn   k $\frac{1}{15}$ turn   l $\frac{1}{40}$ turn?

Use the answers to parts **a** to **l** and calculate how many degrees there are in

m $\frac{3}{4}$ turn   n $\frac{3}{8}$ turn   o $\frac{7}{10}$ turn   p $\frac{5}{6}$ turn

q $\frac{5}{12}$ turn   r $\frac{2}{3}$ turn   s $\frac{2}{5}$ turn   t $\frac{4}{9}$ turn

u $\frac{11}{12}$ turn   v $\frac{13}{15}$ turn   w $\frac{17}{20}$ turn.

10 What fraction of a turn are these angles? Cancel the answers as far as possible.

a $100°$ b $210°$ c $200°$ d $320°$ e $80°$ f $225°$

g $315°$ h $54°$ i $108°$ j $216°$ k $168°$ l $288°$

11 What angle has been turned through in these situations?
Give the answers *both* as a fraction of a turn *and* in degrees.

Face   a   north and turn clockwise to face east

b   east and turn clockwise to face south

c   south and turn clockwise to face north

d   west and turn anticlockwise to face south

e   west and turn clockwise to face south

f   east and turn clockwise to face north

g   SE and turn clockwise to face SW

h   NW and turn anticlockwise to face SE

i   north and turn clockwise to face NE

j   north and turn clockwise to face SE

k   north and turn clockwise to face SW

l   north and turn clockwise to face NW

m   west and turn anticlockwise to face SE

n   SW and turn anticlockwise to face NW.

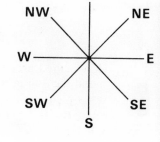

12 **Different types of angles**

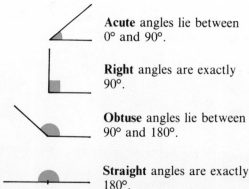

Acute angles lie between $0°$ and $90°$.

Right angles are exactly $90°$.

Obtuse angles lie between $90°$ and $180°$.

Straight angles are exactly $180°$.

Reflex angles lie between $180°$ and $360°$.

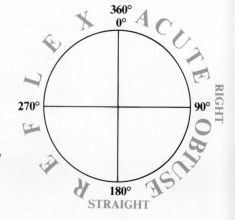

Turns and degrees

What type of angle is each of these?

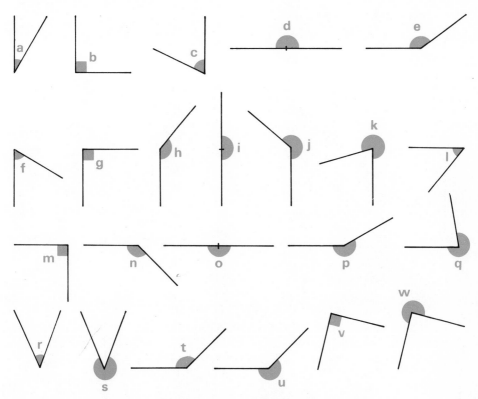

13 Two angles are said to be **supplementary** if they add up to 180°.
Two angles are said to be **complementary** if they add up to 90°.
Are these pairs of angles supplementary, complementary or neither?

a 60°, 30°	b 120°, 60°	c 25°, 45°	d 72°, 18°
e 34°, 56°	f 82°, 98°	g 74°, 116°	h 62°, 38°
i 49°, 41°	j 93°, 87°	k 152°, 38°	l 116°, 64°

14 How many right angles are there in these angles?

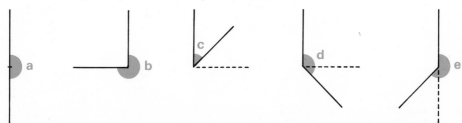

f a clockwise turn from N to E
h a clockwise turn from N to W
j a clockwise turn from N to SE
l a clockwise turn from W to SW

g a clockwise turn from N to S
i a clockwise turn from N to NE
k a clockwise turn from S to NE

Measuring angles

Part 1 Angles less than 180°

Use a protractor to measure these angles.

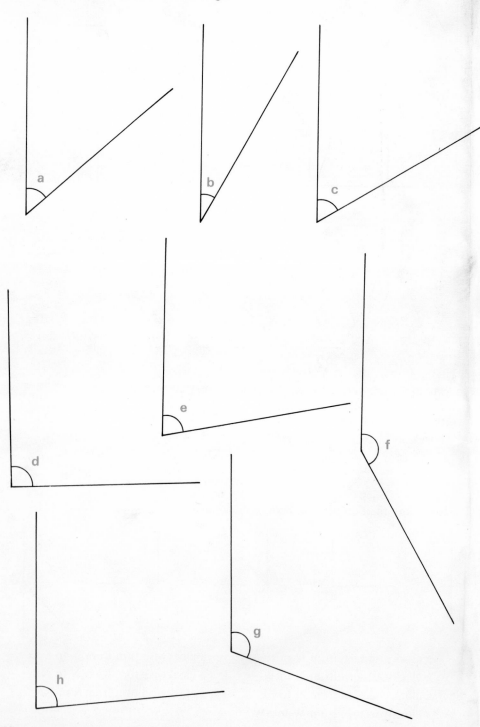

Measuring angles

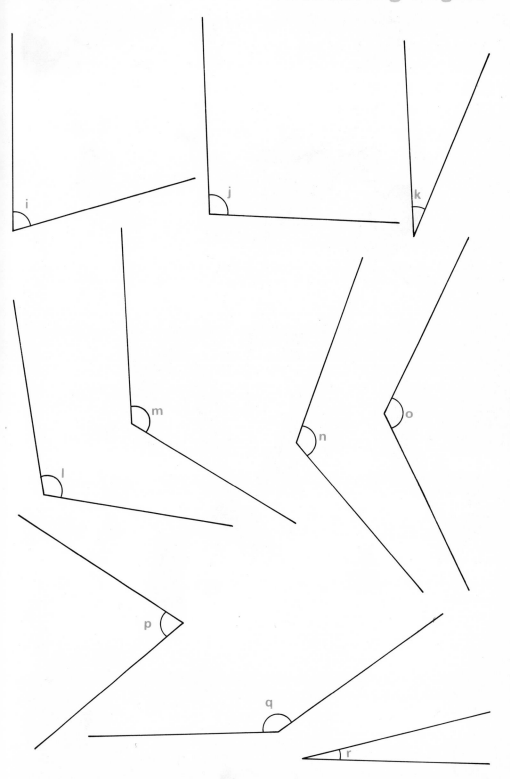

Measuring angles

Part 2 Angles greater than 180°

Use a protractor to measure these angles.

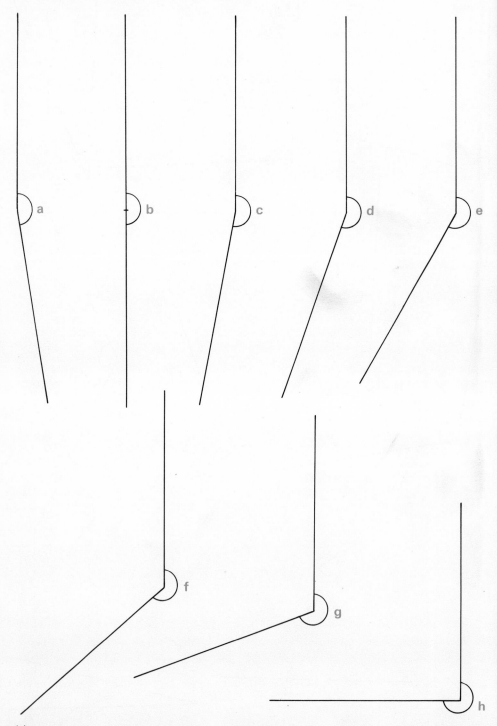

Measuring angles

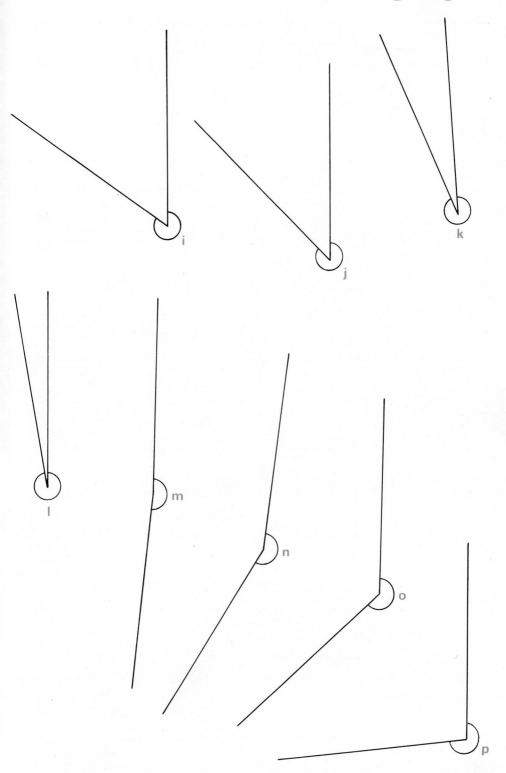

Measuring angles

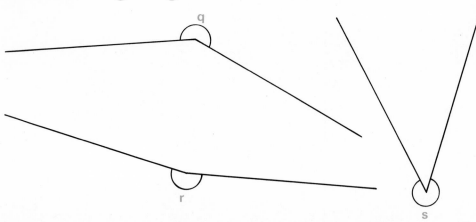

Part 3 A mixture of angles between 0° and 360°

Use a protractor to measure these angles.

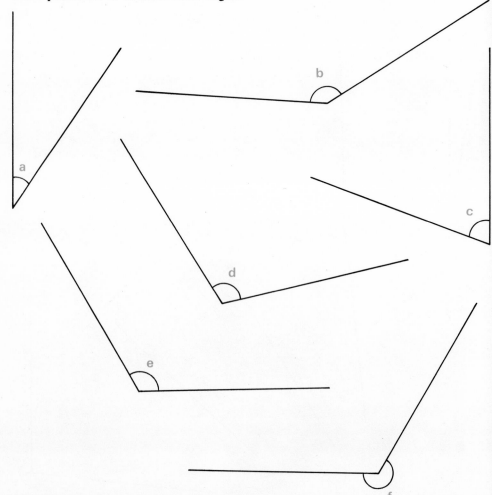

Measuring angles

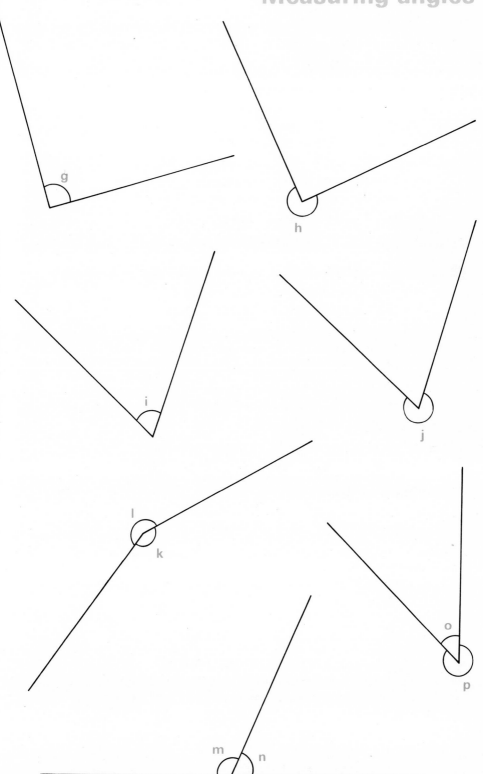

Measuring angles

Part 4 Using axes

1 On cm² paper, draw and label the x-axis from 0 to 18 and the y-axis from 0 to 20.
Plot these sets of three points and join them together. Measure the *acute* or *obtuse* angles using a protractor.

a Plot A(4, 10), B(1, 1), C(9, 1); measure ∠ABC.

b Plot D(1, 10), E(1, 20), F(6, 12); measure ∠DEF.

c Plot G(4, 12), H(7, 3), I(16, 3); measure ∠GHI.

d Plot J(2, 20), K(11, 20), L(17, 13); measure ∠JKL.

e Plot M(6, 19), N(8, 11), O(12, 18); measure ∠MNO.

f Plot P(13, 15), Q(16, 9), R(14, 1); measure ∠PQR.

g Plot S(11, 13), T(8, 7), U(14, 4); measure ∠STU.

2 On cm² paper, draw and label the x-axis from 0 to 18 and the y-axis from 0 to 20.
Plot each of these sets of points; join and measure the required angle.

a Plot A(1, 20), B(1, 14), C(5, 18); measure ∠ABC.

b Plot D(1, 12), E(5, 15), F(4, 9); measure ∠DEF.

c Plot G(1, 10), H(2, 4), I(8, 1); measure ∠GHI.

d Plot J(5, 5), K(11, 5), L(16, 1); measure ∠JKL.

e Plot M(11, 8), N(15, 4), O(16, 10); measure ∠MNO.

f Plot P(6, 9), Q(12, 9), R(13, 15); measure ∠PQR.

g Plot S(6, 13), T(12, 13), U(11, 19); measure ∠STU.

h Plot V(16, 20), W(16, 15), X($15\frac{1}{2}$, 10); measure ∠VWX.

3 On cm² paper draw and label both axes as before.
Plot these sets of three points and join them to make triangles.
Measure the three angles of each triangle and write the results. Add together the three angles for each triangle.

a (1, 1), (7, 1), (7, 8)   b (8, 2), (16, 2), (14, 11)   c (1, 7), (7, 10), (1, 16)

d (1, 20), (5, 14), (9, 18)   e (8, 10), (14, 13), (15, 20)

4 Onto new axes, labelled as before, plot these points and join them to make triangles.
For each triangle, measure its angles, write your measurements and then add together.

a (6, 1), (9, 9), (1, 4)   b (3, 11), (10, 10), (9, 17)   c (1, 7), (0, 14), (3, 20)

d (13, 9), (10, 20), (15, 15)   e (9, 1), (15, 10), (16, 3)

5 On cm² paper draw and label both axes as before.
Plot these sets of five points and join each of them to form a pentagon.
Measure the five angles of each pentagon, write your measurements down and then add together.

a (1, 7), (7, 1), (15, 1), (14, 7), (11, 12)

b (1, 11), (1, 19), (9, 20), (15, 19), (9, 14)

c (3, 17), (6, 10), (15, 8), (16, 14), (9, 18)

Measuring angles

6   Onto new axes, labelled as before, plot these points and join sets of them to form a hexagon.
    For each hexagon, measure its angles, write your measurements and then add together.

    a $(3, 0), (9, 0), (16, 4), (14, 14), (8, 18), (2, 11)$

    b $(1, 20), (9, 20), (16, 15), (16, 9), (6, 10), (1, 14)$

    c $(0, 1), (6, 3), (14, 10), (8, 13), (4, 18), (0, 8)$

Part 5   Accurate drawing

1   Use a protractor, a ruler and a sharp pencil to draw angles of these sizes.

    a   40°   b   65°   c   85°   d   90°   e   95°

    f   120°   g   135°   h   142°   i   178°   j   182°

    k   200°   l   270°   m   300°   n   315°   o   350°

2   Draw four triangles with these angles. The sides can be any length, but the angles must be drawn accurately using a protractor.

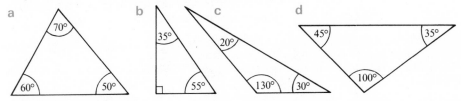

3   Use a ruler and a protractor to draw these quadrilaterals accurately.
    Label the corners, and, for each quadrilateral, measure and write the distance between A and C.

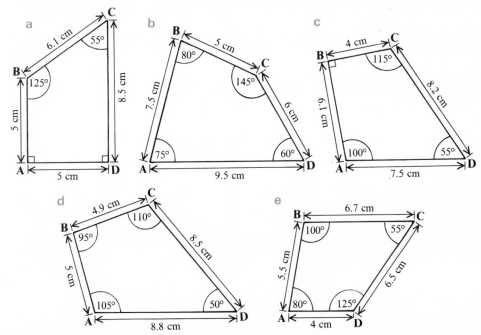

19

Measuring angles

4 The five-sided plot of land shown here is to
be divided into three plots by two fences *AC*
and *AD*.

Using a scale of 1 cm = 10 metres and a ruler
and protractor, make an accurate diagram
of the land.

By taking measurements from the diagram,
find the length of each fence.

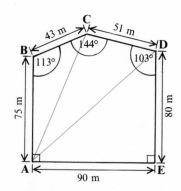

5

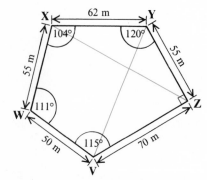

The field *VWXYZ* is to be divided
into four parts by the two fences *VY*
and *XZ*.

Use a scale of 1 cm = 10 metres to
make an accurate diagram of the field.

Take measurements from the diagram
to find the length of each of the fences
VY and *XZ*.

6 A yacht leaves the harbour *H* to sail
to jetty *J*. Its journey is in the four
stages shown.

Use a scale of 1 cm = 1 km to draw
the route accurately.

What is the shortest distance
between *H* and *J*?

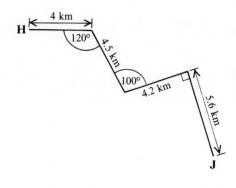

7

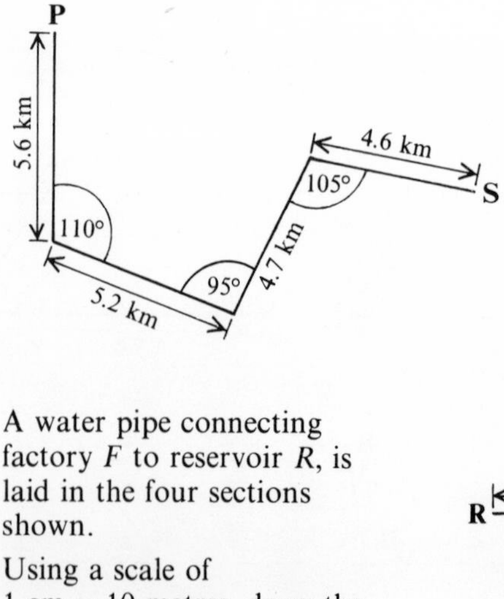

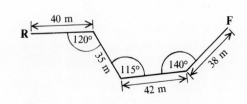

Electricity power lines are carried on
pylons from power-station *P* to
substation *S*.

Using a scale of 1 cm = 1 km, draw
the route accurately and find the
shortest distance between *P* and *S*.

8 A water pipe connecting
factory *F* to reservoir *R*, is
laid in the four sections
shown.

Using a scale of
1 cm = 10 metres, draw the
route accurately and find
the shortest distance
between *R* and *F*.

20

Bearings

Part 1 Introducing three methods

1

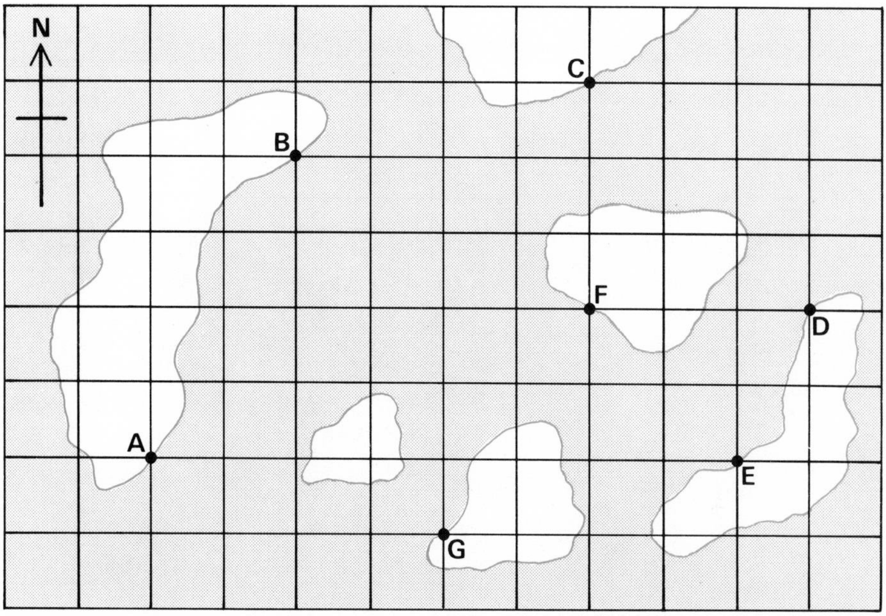

A ship leaves port A and sails to the six other ports on the map, calling at them in alphabetical order, before returning to A.

However, the route must only follow the grid lines of the map, and must, of course, be entirely by sea. Each square of the grid has sides 10 km long.

Copy and complete this table with instructions for the route which must be taken. The route from A to B has been done for you.

From	To	Direction and distance	followed by	Direction and distance
A	B	East 20 km		North 40 km
B	C			
C	D			
D	E			
E	F			
F	G			
G	A			

Bearings

2 This map shows a mariner's compass centred on Cardiff.

The circles have radii of 10, 20, 30 and 40 miles.

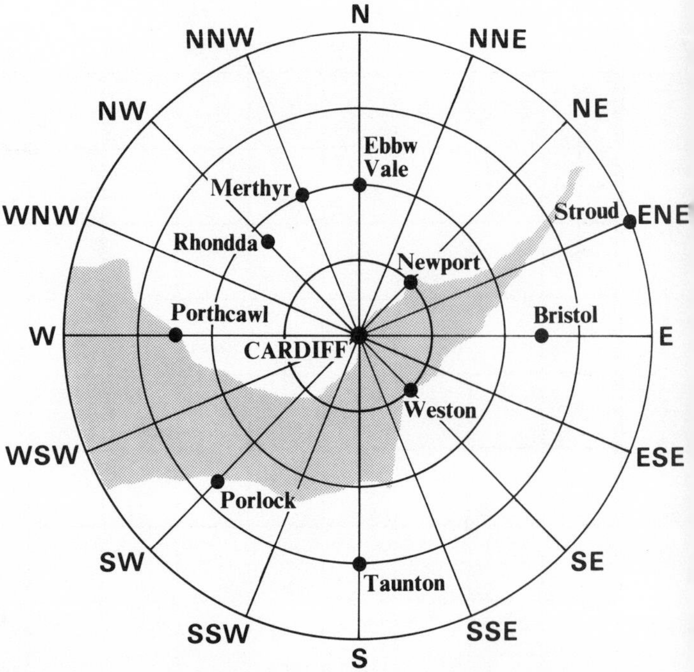

Name the town which is
a due N of Cardiff
b due E of Cardiff
c NW of Cardiff
d SE of Cardiff
e ENE of Cardiff
f NNW of Cardiff.

In what direction from Cardiff is
g Taunton
h Weston
i Rhondda
j Stroud
k Porthcawl
l Newport?

How far is it from Cardiff to
m Newport   n Weston   o Merthyr   p Stroud
q Bristol   r Taunton?

What town is
s 20 miles due N of Cardiff   t 25 miles due W of Cardiff
u 25 miles due E of Cardiff   v 40 miles ENE of Cardiff
w 27 miles SW of Cardiff   x 18 miles NW of Cardiff?

3 Draw a 16-point mariner's compass on tracing-paper.

(Either trace the one in question 2 above or fold the tracing-paper four times to a point.)

By placing the tracing paper on the map on page 23 and taking care to point it to the north, find the bearing of
a Chatham from Worthing   b Hastings from Margate
c Luton from Worthing   d Colchester from Luton
e Hastings from Chatham   f Chatham from Epping
g Croydon from Colchester   h Margate from Chatham
i Epping from Hastings   j Margate from Epping
k Croydon from Luton   l Croydon from Worthing
m Chatham from Colchester.

Bearings

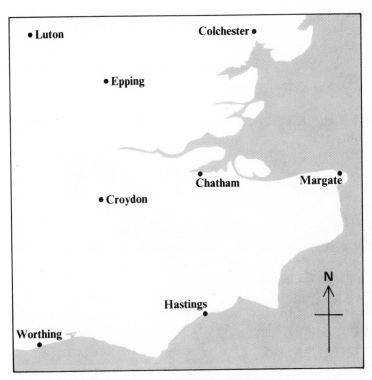

4 There are two other ways of giving a bearing:
   (i)   by facing north or south and turning in either direction
   (ii) by facing north and turning *clockwise*, giving a three-figure number.

Example
   The bearing of *A* from *O* is
   either   S 50° E   *or*   130°.

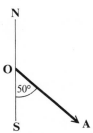 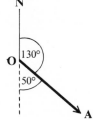

For each of these bearings, draw a diagram and then write the bearing as a three-figure number.

a S 60° E	b S 10° E	c S 80° E	d S 15° E
e S 10° W	f S 30° W	g S 80° W	h S 25° W
i N 40° E	j N 60° E	k N 85° E	l N 13° E
m N 10° W	n N 30° W	o N 80° W	p N 15° W
q NE	r SE	s SW	t NW

Bearings

5   Write each of these as a three-figure bearing, if possible without using a diagram.

   a S 12° E   b S 18° W   c N 52° E   d N 3° W

   e S 42° W   f S 53° E   g N 84° W   h N 19° E

   i S 58° E   j S 76° W   k N 71° W   l N 2° E

6   Write each of these three-figure bearings using the other method. If necessary draw a diagram.

   a 150°   b 195°   c 340°   d 015°

   e 168°   f 202°   g 295°   h 095°

   i 268°   j 301°   k 174°   l 006°

7   *Either* use a 360° protractor *or* make one on tracing-paper.

Place the protractor on this map of Cornwall with the 0° pointing due north, and use the scale which increases clockwise.

Find the three-figure bearing of

   a Boscastle from Penzance   b Truro from Penzance

   c Ilfracombe from Truro   d Plymouth from Boscastle

   e Plymouth from Lundy   f Plymouth from Ilfracombe

   g Penzance from Lundy   h Bude from Ilfracombe

   i Penzance from Plymouth   j Truro from Boscastle

   k Boscastle from Plymouth   l Lundy from Plymouth.

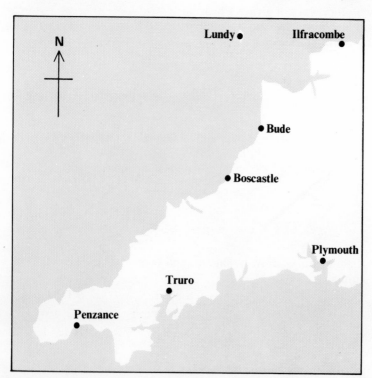

Bearings

8 On squared paper, draw and label the x-axis from 0 to 16 and the y-axis from 0 to 20.

Plot the point Z(8, 10) and draw a north line from Z parallel to the y-axis.

Plot and label each of these points.

Use a protractor to find their three-figure bearings from Z.

A(11, 18)	B(13, 16)	C(12, 14)	D(15, 14)
E(16, 11)	F(14, 10)	G(14, 5)	H(13, 4)
I(15, 0)	J(12, 1)	K(9, 1)	L(8, 4)
M(7, 2)	N(5, 2)	P(3, 4)	Q(1, $7\frac{1}{2}$)
R(3, 10)	S(1, 12)	T(1, 14)	U(3, 16)
V(6, 15)	W(7, 18)	X(16, 7)	Y(2, 6)

9 Write each of these as a three-figure bearing.

a	due South	b	due East	c	due West	d	SE
e	NE	f	SSE	g	ESE	h	SSW
i	WSW	j	ENE	k	NNW	l	WNW

Bearings

Part 2 Three-figure bearings

Bearings

Trace this map of the British Isles and northern France and mark on it all the towns and cities as shown.

Draw a north line through Cardiff and use a protractor to answer these questions.

1. What is the bearing of Middlesbrough from Cardiff?
2. What is the bearing of Cambridge from Cardiff?
3. What is the bearing of London from Cardiff?
4. What is the bearing of Dieppe from Cardiff?
5. What is the bearing of St Malo from Cardiff?
6. What is the bearing of Plymouth from Cardiff?
7. What is the bearing of Cork from Cardiff?
8. What is the bearing of Galway from Cardiff?

Draw a north line through Glasgow to answer these questions.

9. What is the bearing of Inverness from Glasgow?
10. What is the bearing of Newcastle from Glasgow?
11. What is the bearing of Londonderry from Glasgow?

Draw north lines as required to answer these next questions.

12. What is the bearing of Dieppe from London?
13. What is the bearing of Paris from London?
14. What is the bearing of St Malo from Paris?
15. What is the bearing of Paris from St Malo?
16. What is the bearing of Galway from Dieppe?
17. What is the bearing of Dieppe from Galway?
18. What is the bearing of Glasgow from Plymouth?
19. What is the bearing of Plymouth from Glasgow?
20. What is the bearing of London from Paris?

The scale of the map is   1 mm = 7 km   or   1 cm = 70 km.

Use a ruler to answer these problems.

21. Write the distance in kilometres between

   a Plymouth and St Malo
   b Cardiff and Dieppe
   c Inverness and Cambridge
   d Inverness and London
   e Galway and St Malo
   f Londonderry and Newcastle
   g Plymouth and Middlesbrough
   h Paris and Londonderry
   i Plymouth and Dieppe
   j Cork and Glasgow
   k Dieppe and Londonderry
   l Glasgow and Paris.

22. Find the town on this map which is approximately

   a 350 km from London
   b 490 km from Cardiff
   c 560 km from Cork
   d 910 km from Inverness
   e 245 km from Glasgow
   f 595 km from London
   g 595 km from St Malo
   h 245 km from Cambridge.

27

Bearings

23 a How far is it from Land's End to John o' Groats?
   b On what bearing is John o' Groats from Land's End?
   c On what bearing is Land's End from John o' Groats?

24 How many sets of three towns which are in line with each other are to be found on this map?

Part 3   Scale diagrams

A protractor, a ruler and a sharp pencil will be needed to draw these scale diagrams accurately, and thus to answer the questions.

For each diagram, label the north line.

Use a scale of 1 cm = 10 metres for the first seven diagrams.

1 A tree is on a bearing of 060° from you and is 40 metres away.
A gate is on a bearing of 090° from you and is 60 metres away.
How far is the tree from the gate?

2 A hill is on a bearing of 050° from you and is 60 metres away.
A bridge is on a bearing of 100° from you and is 50 metres away.
How far is the hill from the bridge?

3 A bus stop is on a bearing of 080° from you and is 30 m away.
A manhole is on a bearing of 120° from you and is 40 m away.
A house is on a bearing of 140° from you and is 35 m away.
How far is it from the bus stop to the house?
How far is it from the house to the manhole?

4 A car is 30 m away from you on a bearing of 060°.
A bus is 38 m away from you on a bearing of 150°.
A van is 42 m away from you on a bearing of 190°.
How far is the bus from the van and how far is the bus from the car?

5 A pylon is 44 m away from you on a bearing of 120°.
A barn is 52 m away from you on a bearing of 200°.
A cottage is 34 m away from you on a bearing of 220°.
How far is the barn from the pylon and how far is the barn from the cottage?

6 A church spire is 27 m from you on a bearing of 010°.
A signpost is 30 m from you on a bearing of 180°.
A park gate is 46 m from you on a bearing of 210°.
A road junction is 40 m from you on a bearing of 280°.
How far is the spire from the signpost?
How far is the park gate from the road junction?
How far is the park gate from the church spire?

7 A caravan is 34 m from you on a bearing of 190°.
A shop door is 52 m away from you on a bearing of 222°.
An archway is 18 m away on a bearing of 305°.
A lorry is 26 m away on a bearing of 340°.
How far is the caravan from the lorry?
How far is the archway from the shop door?
How far is the shop door from the lorry?

Bearings

Now use a scale of 1 cm = 10 km.

8　You are standing on a hill top.
A church tower is 20 km from you on a bearing of 046°.
A power station is 47 km from you on a bearing of 137°.
A television mast is 32 km from you on a bearing of 165°.
How far is the power station from the TV mast?
How far is the church tower from the power station?

9　You live in a village in the country.
The town of Arlton is 46 km from your home on a bearing of 035°.
The village of Barnby is 27 km from your home on a bearing of 151°.
The town of Carnwich is 34 km from your home on a bearing of 220°.
What is the distance between
　a　Arlton and Carnwich　　　　　b　Barnby and Carnwich?

10　You are a lighthouse keeper.
An oil tanker is 52 km away from you on a bearing of 145°.
A cargo boat is 18 km from you on a bearing of 195°.
A passenger liner is 43 km from you on a bearing of 280°.
How far apart are
　a　the oil tanker and the cargo boat　　　　b　the cargo boat and the liner?

11　You spend a night in a youth hostel in a mountainous area.
Ben More is 12 km from the hostel on a bearing of 154°.
Ben Shader is 43 km from the hostel on a bearing of 202°.
Ben Assait is 37 km from the hostel on a bearing of 300°.
How far is
　a　Ben More from Ben Shader　　　　b　Ben More from Ben Assait?

12　You live in the centre of Preston.
Lancaster is 32 km from Preston on a bearing of 345°.
Liverpool is 45 km from Preston on a bearing of 210°.
Manchester is 40 km from Preston on a bearing of 140°.
Halifax is 56 km from Preston on a bearing of 095°.
What is the distance between
　a　Lancaster and Liverpool　　　　b　Halifax and Manchester?

Use a scale of 1 cm = 100 km.

13　You are the pilot of an aeroplane based in London.
Paris is 350 km on a bearing of 150° from London.
Amsterdam is 370 km on a bearing of 072° from London.
Dublin is 450 km on a bearing of 300° from London.
How far do you fly if you go
　a　from London to Dublin and back
　b　on a circuit from London to Amsterdam, then to Paris and finally back to London?

14　You are an airline pilot based in Helsinki, Finland.
Leningrad is 300 km from Helsinki on a bearing of 095°.
Stockholm is 410 km from Helsinki on a bearing of 260°.
Umea is 470 km from Helsinki on a bearing of 330°.
You leave Helsinki and touch down at Leningrad, Stockholm and Umea in this order before returning to Helsinki. How far have you flown?

Bearings

Part 4   The Shetland Isles

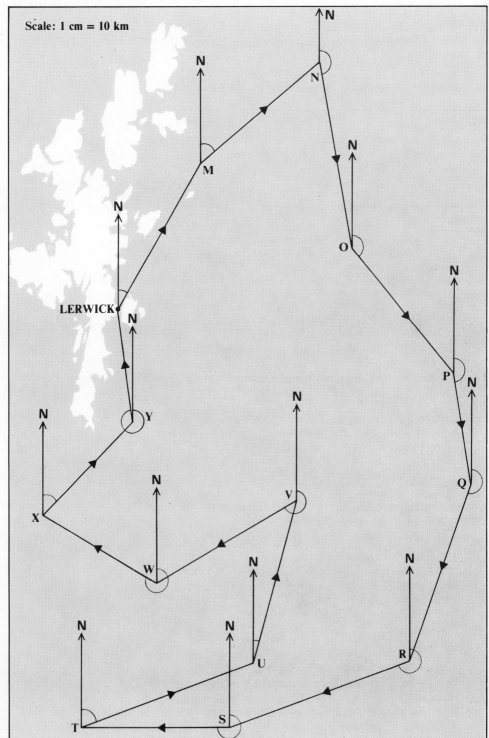

Scale: 1 cm = 10 km

LERWICK

N M N O P Q R S T U V W X Y

Bearings

This map of the Shetland Isles shows the course taken by a fishing boat which leaves the town of Lerwick *L*, to sail to points *M, N, O, P, Q* .... *Y* before returning to Lerwick.

For each stage of the journey, use a protractor to measure its bearing and a ruler to measure its distance.

Copy and complete this table and enter the results.

	the bearing	the distance
M from *L*		
N from *M*		
O from *N*		
P from *O*		
L from *Y*		

Part 5   Bearings and journeys

A protractor, a ruler and a sharp pencil will be needed to draw these scale diagrams accurately and thus solve the problems.

On each diagram draw a north line at each point where a bearing is taken.

For the first six diagrams, use a scale of 1 cm = 10 metres.

1   You set off on a bearing of 060° and walk 50 m, then you turn onto a new bearing of 100° and walk 60 m. How far are you from your starting point?

2   You set off on a bearing of 050° and walk 68 m, then you turn onto a new bearing of 090° and walk 45 m. How far are you from your starting point?

3   A man walks on a bearing of 085° for 48 m and then turns onto a bearing of 140° and walks for another 75 m. How far is he now from his starting point?

4   Frank leaves his home on a bearing of 100° and walks 65 m to arrive at the street corner. He then turns onto a bearing of 040° and walks 45 m to reach the bus stop.
What is the shortest distance between his home and the bus stop?

5   A surveyor draws a line on a road to show workmen where to lay a pipe.
The line starts on a bearing of 010° and goes for 35 m before it turns onto a bearing of 110° and continues for another 53 m. It then makes another turn onto a bearing of 200° for the final section of 43 m.
What will be the shortest distance between the two ends of the pipe?

6   Judy has to walk from the car-park on a bearing of 135° for 42 m to reach the school gate. She then turns onto a bearing of 220° and walks 51 m to reach the school door. She turns again onto a new bearing of 280° and walks 22 m to reach her class-room.
How far is it directly from the car-park to the class-room?

Bearings

Use a scale of 1 cm = 10 km for these diagrams.

7   A hiker walks 44 km from a village on a bearing of 065° to reach a hilltop. On the hilltop he turns to a bearing of 120° and walks 32 km to reach a railway station. Here he catches a train which takes him 28 km on a bearing of 240° to reach his home town.
How far is his home town from the village by the shortest route?

8   A helicopter leaves an airport and flies 62 km on a bearing of 130° to reach the village of Lampton. It then leaves Lampton on a bearing of 015° and flies 74 km to land at Monksby. Finally it leaves Monksby on a bearing of 205° and flies 33 km to reach Norton.
a   How far has the helicopter flown altogether?
b   What is the direct distance from the airport to Norton?

9   An electricity company is laying a new line of pylons from a power station to the town of Nolyteson.
The line leaves the power station on a bearing of 024° and travels 54 km straight to point A. From A the line turns onto a bearing of 300° and goes direct to point B 36 km away. At B the line changes direction onto a bearing of 255° and Nolyteson is 41 km away in this direction. Find
a   the total length of the line of pylons
b   the direct distance from the power station to the town.

10   A commando is given these instructions to get from the shore where he is dropped to the enemy camp.
From the shore, walk 12 km on a bearing of 105° to a village.
From the village, go 24 km on a bearing of 206° to a river bridge.
From the bridge, go 46 km on a bearing of 185° to a railway station.
From the station, go 34 km on a bearing of 082° to the enemy camp.
a   How far does the commando have to travel if he follows these instructions?
b   What is the shortest distance between the coast and the enemy camp?

11   A guided missile is tracking a rocket and it follows this course.
After being fired from its launching pad, it travels 46 km on a bearing of 254°. It then turns onto a bearing of 097° and travels a further 72 km. Another turn changes its bearing to 006° and in 24 km it strikes the rocket.
How far is it from the launching pad when it hits the rocket?

Use a scale of 1 cm = 100 km for these diagrams.

12   A private yacht starts a Mediterranean cruise at Valencia in Spain.
It sails 650 km on a bearing of 050° to reach Toulon in France. Leaving Toulon on a bearing of 084°, it sails 350 km to Leghorn in Italy. From Leghorn it sails 640 km on a bearing of 157° to arrive at Palermo in Sicily.
a   How far has the yacht sailed altogether?
b   If it had sailed straight from Valencia to Palermo by the shortest route, how far would the yacht have travelled and on what bearing?

13   A Caribbean cargo boat leaves Barbados on a bearing of 215° to make the 360 km trip to Trinidad. It leaves Trinidad to sail 840 km on a bearing of 280° to Curaçao. Leaving Curaçao on a bearing of 048° it sails 900 km to reach St Kitts.
a   How far has the cargo boat sailed altogether?
b   If it had gone straight to St Kitts from Barbados, what distance would the boat have covered and on what bearing?

14   An airline plans the following route for one of its planes.
It leaves London on a bearing of 148° for Paris 340 km away. From Paris on a
bearing of 070° it flies 470 km to Frankfurt. From Frankfurt on a bearing
of 180° it flies 320 km to Zurich. Finally, it flies from Zurich 750 km on a
bearing of 252° to Bordeaux.
a   How far has the aircraft flown?
b   If it had flown direct from London to Bordeaux, how far would the aircraft
have travelled and on what bearing?

15   A racing yacht sails clockwise on a square course, the first side of which is
450 km on a bearing of 015°.
Draw the course to scale and write the bearings it must follow to complete the
other three sides of the square.

Polar co-ordinates

Part 1

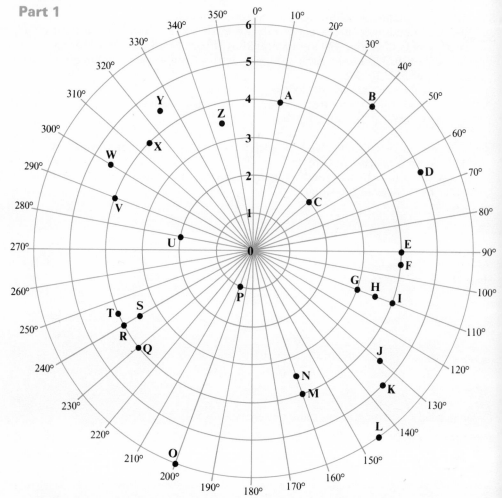

1 Write the polar co-ordinates of these lettered points. For example, $A = (4, 10°)$

2 Several sheets of polar paper with ten concentric circles 1 cm apart will be required.
Label the radii from 0° to 350° and label the circles from 1 to 10.
Join these points with straight lines in the order given. What shapes do they make?

Shapes **1** to **4** can be drawn on the same sheet.

Shape 1 $(10, 30°), (8, 60°), (7, 40°), (3, 50°), (3, 10°), (7, 20°), (8, 0°), (10, 30°)$

Shape 2 $(6, 70°), (7, 90°), (9, 90°), (7\frac{1}{2}, 100°), (9, 110°), (7, 110°), (6, 130°), (5, 110°),$
$(3, 100°), (5, 90°), (6, 70°)$

Shape 3 $(4, 210°), (5, 230°), (4, 220°), (3, 210°), (3, 190°), (4, 180°), (5, 180°), (6, 160°),$
$(6, 140°), (8, 170°), (8, 180°), (9, 180°), (9, 190°), (8, 180°), (8, 190°),$
$(7, 200°), (5, 210°), (5, 230°)$
Draw an eye at $(3\frac{1}{2}, 210°)$.

Shape 4 $(4, 240°), (7, 260°), (9, 280°), (7, 300°), (5, 310°), (5, 340°), (4, 350°), (3, 360°),$
$(2, 290°), (2, 250°), (4, 240°), (6, 290°), (7, 260°)$
Draw an eye at $(3, 280°)$ and join $(4, 310°)$ to $(5, 340°)$.

34

Polar co-ordinates

Shapes **5** to **8** can be drawn on the same sheet.

Shape 5 (5, 30°), (7, 25°), (9, 30°), (10, 40°), (10, 55°), (8, 65°), (8, 55°), (7, 60°),
(7, 70°), (5, 90°), (5, 80°), (4, 70°), (3, 60°), (2, 60°), (1½, 20°), (2½, 20°),
(3, 10°), (4½, 20°), (5, 30°)
Draw an eye at (3, 20°) and another at (4, 30°).

Shape 6 (7, 280°), (3½, 290°), (6, 290°), (7, 285°), (7, 280°), (8, 270°), (8, 260°), (7, 250°),
(4, 240°), (2, 260°), (2, 290°), (1, 320°), (1½, 310°), (2, 330°), (2½, 300°),
(3, 280°), (3½, 290°)

Shape 7 (4, 190°), (3, 200°), (2, 190°), (3, 180°), (4, 190°), (4, 180°), (5, 170°), (4, 160°),
(6, 170°), (5, 180°), (7, 185°), (9, 180°), (10, 175°), (9, 185°), (7, 190°),
(9, 190°), (10, 200°), (9, 195°), (7, 195°), (5, 200°), (6, 220°), (5, 210°),
(4, 200°), (4, 190°)

Shape 8 (8, 285°), (8, 295°), (7, 305°), (8, 310°), (9, 320°), (10, 310°), (9, 330°), (10, 340°),
(9, 340°), (9, 330°), (8, 330°), (8, 340°), (7½, 330°), (8, 325°), (7, 320°),
(5½, 330°), (6, 340°), (5, 330°), (7, 315°), (6, 310°), (7½, 295°), (8, 285°)

A separate sheet of polar paper will be needed for each of shapes **9** and **10**.

Shape 9 (1.2, 0°), (6.2, 79°), (7.2, 59°), (8.5, 63°), (7.5, 108°), (10, 130°),
(9, 137°), (5.7, 117°), (2.5, 180°), (7, 200°), (8, 216°), (3.5, 225°),
(4.5, 304°), (5, 270°), (8, 289°), (7.3, 320°), (6, 350°), (1.2, 0°)

Shape 10 (4.5, 56°), (7, 122°), (8.2, 116°), (9, 123°), (7, 135°), (3.7, 90°),
(5, 180°), (5.5, 207°), (3.7, 270°), (7, 225°), (9, 236°), (7.5, 235°), (4.5, 303°),
(6.5, 315°), (7.2, 329°), (4, 340°), (3.5, 315°), (1.2, 180°), (4.5, 56°)

Part 2 Plotting curves

Copy and complete each table using the equation given.

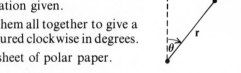

Plot the points (r, θ) from each table and join them all together to give a
smooth curve. r is in centimetres and θ is measured clockwise in degrees.

These first five curves can be drawn on one sheet of polar paper.
Label each curve with its equation.

1 $r = \dfrac{\theta}{10}$

θ	0°	10°	20°	30°	40°	50°	60°	70°	80°	90°	100°
r											

2 $r = \dfrac{\theta}{20}$

θ	0°	20°	40°	60°	80°	100°	120°	140°	160°	180°	200°
r											

3 $r = \dfrac{\theta}{30}$

θ	0°	30°	60°	90°	120°	150°	180°	210°	240°	270°	300°
r											

4 $r = \dfrac{\theta}{40}$

θ	0°	20°	40°	60°	80°	100°	120°	... and in steps of 20° up to ... 400°
r								

5 $r = \dfrac{\theta}{50}$

θ	0°	25°	50°	75°	100°	125°	... and in steps of 25° up to ... 500°
r							

Polar co-ordinates

6 Use another sheet of polar paper for the curve with the equation $r = \dfrac{\theta}{100}$.
   Take $\theta = 0°, 50°, 100°, 150°, 200°, \ldots$ and in steps of $50°$ up to $1000°$.
   Plot the points and draw a smooth curve through them.

7 An interesting pattern can be drawn using six similar curves with the equation
   $\theta = 20r + n$, where $n = 0°, 60°, 120°, 180°, 240°$ and $300°$.

   Copy this table and complete the six rows using the different values of n.

r	0	1	2	3	4	5	6	7	8	9	10
θ when $n = 0°$											
θ when $n = 60°$											
θ when $n = 120°$											
θ when $n = 180°$											
θ when $n = 240°$											
θ when $n = 300°$											

Part 3   On a radar screen

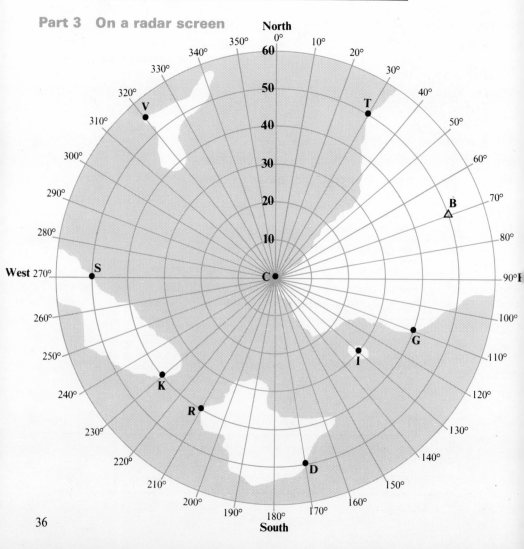

Polar co-ordinates

A radar screen is like a circular television screen with concentric circles marked on it. The radar screen shown here is centred on a coastguard station *C* and shows the coastline of several islands. Its scale is 1 cm = 10 km.

1   Write the polar co-ordinates of
   a   Tarbert, *T*
   b   Ben More, *B*
   c   Innismor, *I*
   d   Glawick, *G*
   e   Dunvaig, *D*
   f   Rubha Point, *R*
   g   Kyleaig, *K*
   h   Stacpay, *S*
   i   Vateray, *V*.

2   Use a ruler to find the shortest distance, in kilometres, between
   a   Tarbert and Ben More
   b   Stacpay and Vateray
   c   Kyleaig and Innismor
   d   Vateray and Tarbert
   e   Innismore and Glawick
   f   Rubha Point and Kyleaig
   g   Dunvaig and Innismor
   h   Kyleaig and Stacpay
   i   Vateray and Dunvaig.

3   A long-distance footpath starts at Tarbert and goes to Glawick via the summit of Ben More. It then leaves Glawick and heads direct for the coastguard station. How long is the footpath?

4   A party of bird-watchers sets sail from Tarbert to go to Innismor. The boat has to go via Stacpay to take on supplies. What is the total distance travelled on arrival at Innismor?

5   Dunvaig is supplied with electricity from Tarbert by an overland powerline from Tarbert to Glawick, and then by an undersea cable from Glawick to Dunvaig. What is the total distance that the power is carried?

6   A small boat is in difficulties exactly halfway between Rubha Point and the coastguard station. How far has a lifeboat from Stacpay to travel to reach the small boat?

7   A yacht leaves Stacpay on a three-stage journey. It sails direct to Vateray and from there to Rubha Point before continuing to Kyleaig. What is the total distance it has to travel?

8   A light aircraft service connects the three large islands with Glawick. One round trip leaves Glawick for Vateray, then on to Kyleaig and finally Dunvaig, before returning to Glawick. Find the distance covered on this journey.

Several sheets of polar paper with ten concentric circles 1 cm apart will be required. Label the radii from 0° to 350° and the circles from 1 to 10.

Problems **9, 10, 11** and **12** can be done on one sheet with a scale of 1 cm = 10 km.

9   A ship appears on the radar screen at the point (10, 15°) and follows a course given by the points (10, 15°), (8, 30°), (9, 50°), (10, 80°), joined in this order by straight lines. The ship then disappears from the screen at the point (10, 80°).
   a   Measure the lengths of the three sections of its course and find the total distance it is seen to travel.
   b   If it covers this distance in 5 hours, what is the ship's average speed in km/h?

10   A yacht sails on a triangular course with corners at (5, 60°), (7, 115°) and (10, 100°).
   a   Draw the course and use a ruler to find the total length of one lap of the course.
   b   If the yacht completes one lap in 10 hours, what is its average speed?

Polar co-ordinates

11 A salvage boat leaves a port P (3, 160°) and heads directly towards a lighthouse L (8, 190°). At L it turns and sails to a wreck W (7, 205°).
   a Mark and label P, L and W on the diagram and draw the course of the boat.
   b How far did the boat sail from P to reach W?
   c It leaves W and sails back to P by the shortest possible route. How many kilometres has the boat to travel on this return trip?

12 An area of sea in the shape of a rectangle is used as the testing ground for rockets. The area has corners at (9, 240°), (9, 300°), (7, 310°) and (7, 230°). Draw the area and find
   a the length (in km) of the rocket range   b the width (in km) of the range
   c the area (in km²) of the range.

Label another sheet of polar paper as before.

Problems **13**, **14**, **15** and **16** can be done on this one sheet with a scale of 1 cm = 10 km.

13 The coastline is shown on a radar screen as four straight lines joining (10, 340°), (8, 0°), (8, 15°), (8, 40°) and (10, 55°) in this order. By using a ruler, find the total length (in km) of the coastline shown on the screen.

14 A fishing boat leaves the harbour H (8, 40°) on a four-stage trip shown by joining these points in order:
   (8, 40°), (8, 85°), (4½, 100°), (5½, 20°), (8, 40°).
   a Find how many kilometres the boat sails in total on this trip.
   b If it takes ten hours for the journey, what is its average speed in km/h?

15 A rectangular area of sea is forbidden to fishing. The corners of the rectangle are (6, 150°), (10, 190°), (8, 225°), (1½, 220°).
   a Draw the area and write the length and breadth of the rectangle in kilometres.
   b Calculate the area of the sea enclosed within this rectangle, to two significant figures.

16 Three lightships are anchored at the corners of an isosceles triangle A(10, 320°), B(9, 275°), C(4, 280°).
   a Plot and label the triangle ABC and find the shortest distance the lightkeeper at A has to travel to visit both the lightships B and C and return to A.
   b What is the shortest distance from A to the line joining B and C?
   c Calculate the area (in km²) of the sea inside the triangle ABC.

Problems **17**, **18**, **19** and **20** can be done on another sheet of polar paper.

Label it as before, but now use a scale of 1 cm = 1 km.

17 The radar screen shows a harbour H at (10, 60°), and three ships A(9, 10°), B(6, 40°) and C(3, 50°). Plot H, A, B, and C.
   a How far (in km) is ship A from harbour H?
   b How far (in km) is ship A from ship B?
   c How far (in km) is ship C from harbour H?
   d A helicopter leaves harbour H to visit all three ships in the order A, B, C and then returns to H. Draw its route and find how many kilometres it flies.

Polar co-ordinates

18 The radar screen shows two lighthouses $L(4, 100°)$ and $M(9, 130°)$ being visited by a supply ship S starting from $(4, 150°)$. The ship S travels first to lighthouse L and then goes from L direct to M. After visiting M it returns to harbour H at $(10, 60°)$.

   a Find the distance in km between the lighthouses L and M.
   b Find how far lighthouse M is from harbour H.
   c Draw the route of the ship S from the starting point $(4, 150°)$ to harbour H and find the total distance it sails.

19 Three buoys B_1 $(5, 220°)$, B_2 $(10, 230°)$ and B_3 $(7, 190°)$ mark three corners of a triangle inside which all fishing is forbidden.

   a Find the distance in km between buoys B_2 and B_3.
   b Draw the shortest distance from B_1 to the line joining B_2 and B_3 and find this distance in km.
   c Calculate the area in km^2 of the triangle $B_1B_2B_3$, to two significant figures.

20 Three flags F_1 $(4, 280°)$, F_2 $(9, 300°)$ and F_3 $(7, 350°)$ mark the three corners of a triangular course for a high-speed boat race. The boats start at F_1 and visit F_2, F_3 and return to F_1 on each lap of the race. They have to do twelve laps to complete the race. Find

   a the length in km of one lap of the race
   b the total length of the race to the nearest km
   c the time taken by a boat which averages a speed of 100 km/h
   d the area in km^2 of the sea inside the triangular course.

Problems **21**, **22**, **23** and **24** can be drawn on one sheet of polar paper.

Label it as before and use a scale of 1 cm = 1 km.

21 A ship S at $(6, 330°)$ is to sail to port $P(9, 80°)$, but it must keep to the north of three buoys at $(7, 350°)$, $(8, 20°)$, $(9, 50°)$. Plot these positions and draw the shortest possible route for the ship onto the polar paper.
Find the length in km of this route.

22 A yacht capsizes and a search is made for it inside the triangle with corners at $(3, 140°)$, $(10, 130°)$ and $(9, 190°)$. Find by taking measurements with a ruler, the area of the sea which is being searched, to the nearest km^2.

23 Four oil rigs are positioned at these points:
$R_1(3, 200°)$, $R_2(7, 210°)$, $R_3(9, 230°)$ and $R_4(5, 240°)$.
A helicopter leaves port P at $(9, 80°)$ and flies directly to R_1, and then visits all four rigs in the order given above, before flying straight back to P from R_4. Draw the route taken by the helicopter and find the total distance it has travelled.

24 An area of the sea is too shallow for shipping. It has the shape of a quadrilateral with corners at $(9, 260°)$, $(7, 280°)$, $(3, 290°)$ and $(10, 310°)$. Join the points $(9, 260°)$ and $(3, 290°)$ to form two triangles and take measurements with a ruler to find the area of this dangerous region, to the nearest km^2.

Points and lines

Part 1   Full turns

Find the sizes of the lettered angles in these diagrams.
Angles marked with the same letter are equal.

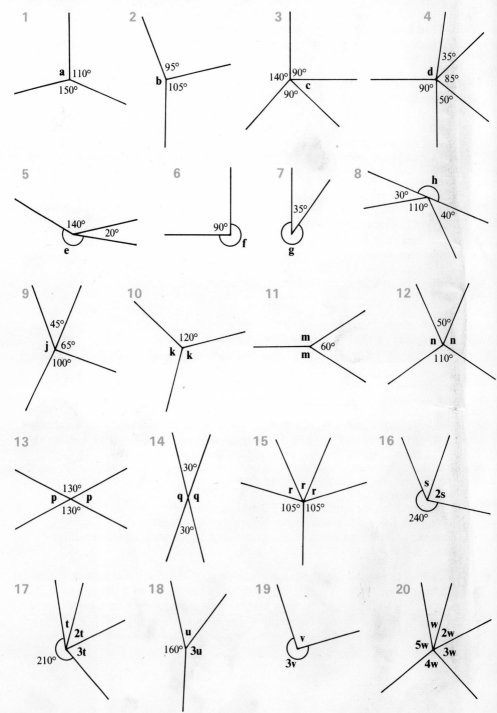

Points and lines

Part 2   Straight lines or half turns

Find the sizes of the lettered angles in these diagrams.
Angles marked with the same letter are equal.

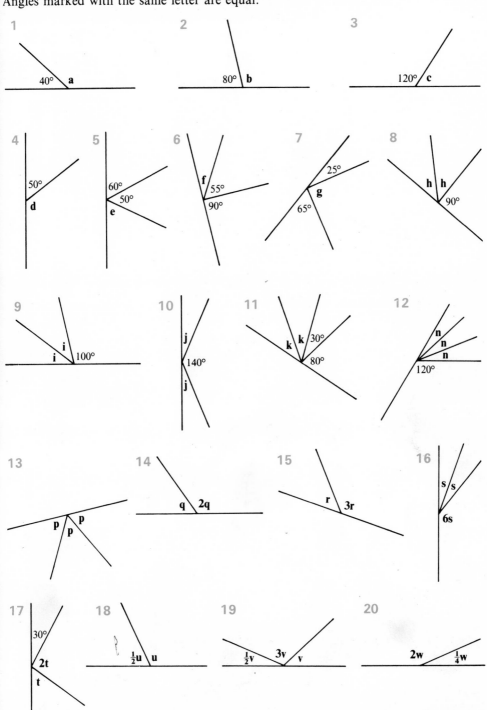

Points and lines

Part 3 Vertically opposite angles

Find the sizes of the lettered angles in these diagrams.
Angles marked with the same letter are equal.

1
150° c
b a

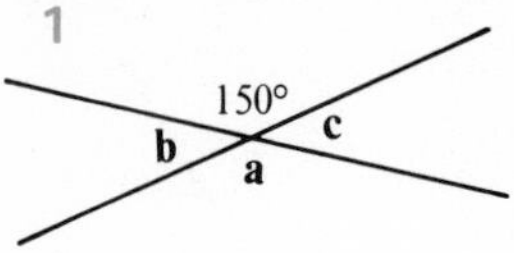

2
120° f
e d

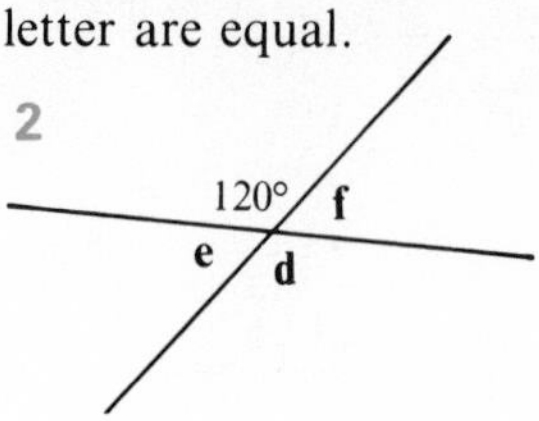

3
g h
40° i

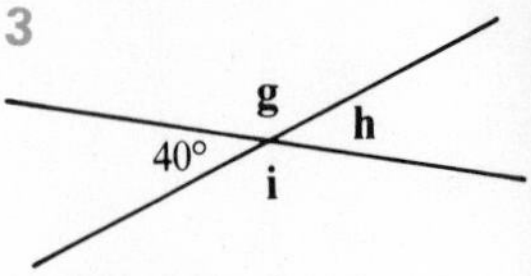

4
j 90°
k

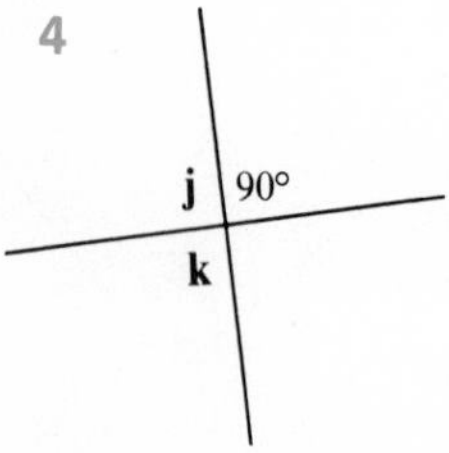

5
l 75°
m n

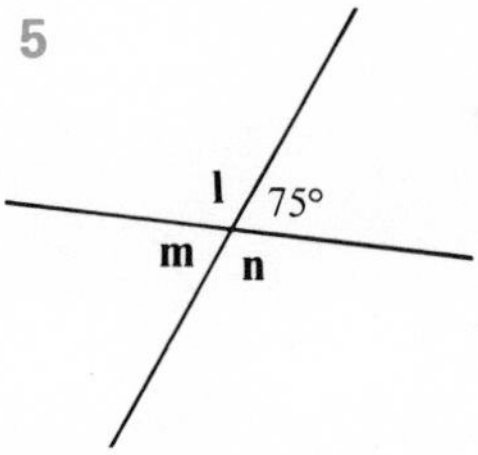

6
z y
130° y

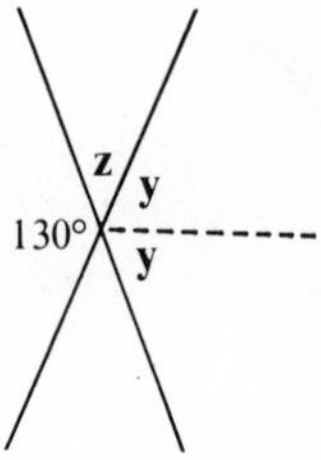

7
160°
p p q

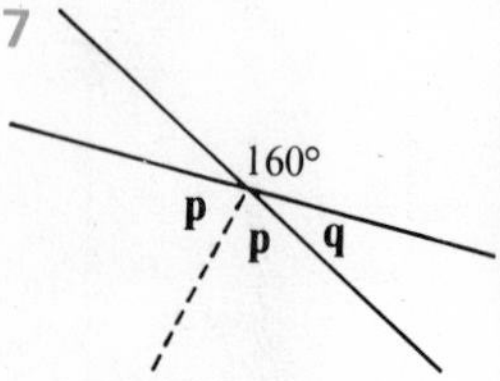

8
c c c
d
120°

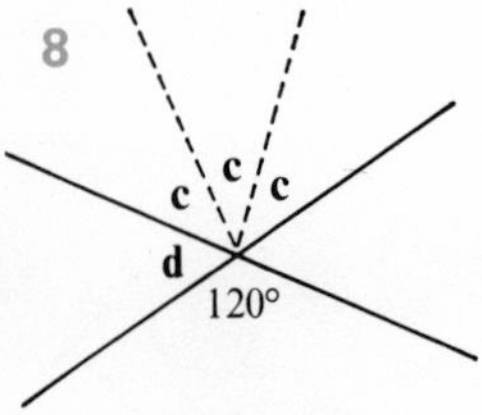

9
s s
40°
t

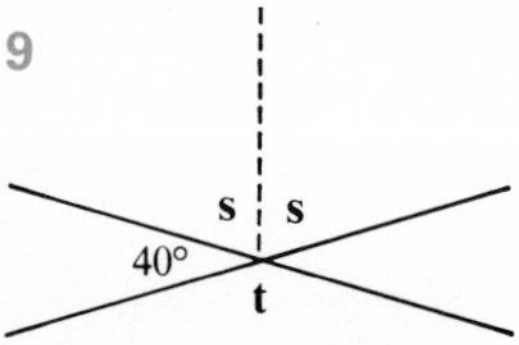

10 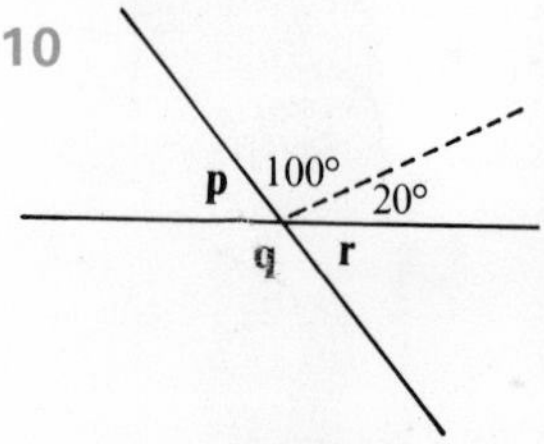
p 100°
20°
q r

11 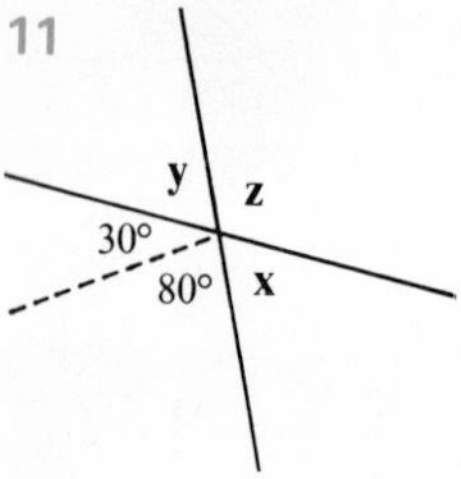
y z
30°
80° x

12 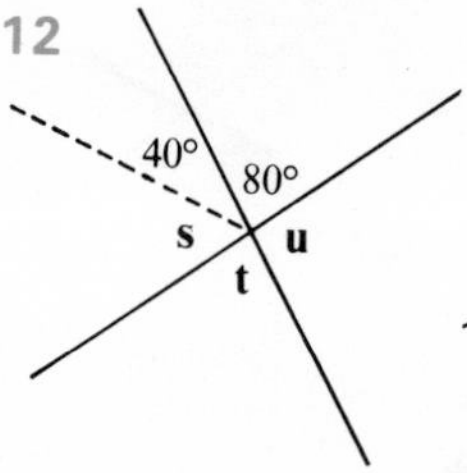
40° 80°
s u
t

13 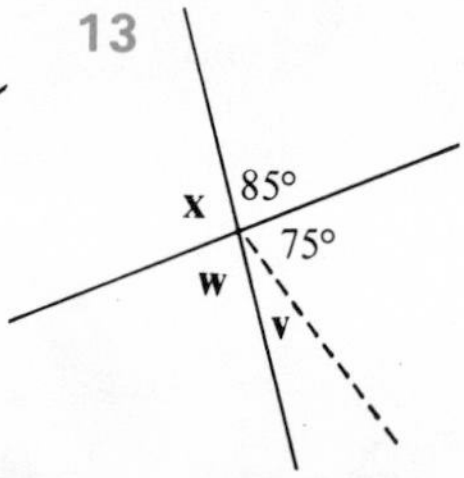
x 85°
75°
w
v

14 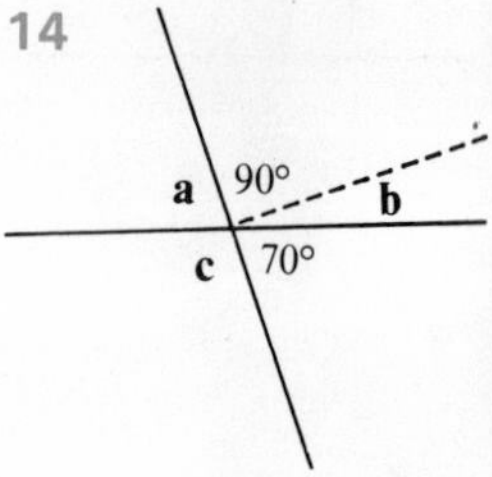
a 90°
b
c 70°

15 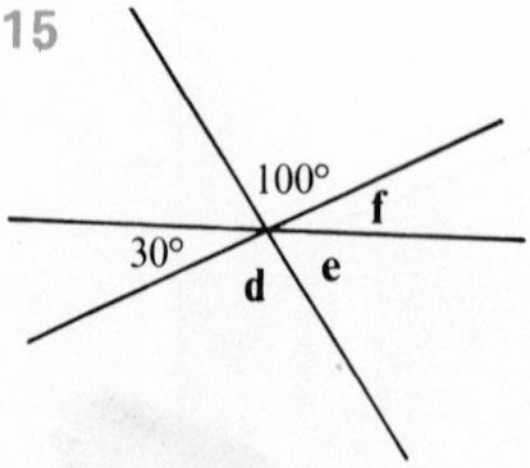
100° f
30°
d e

16 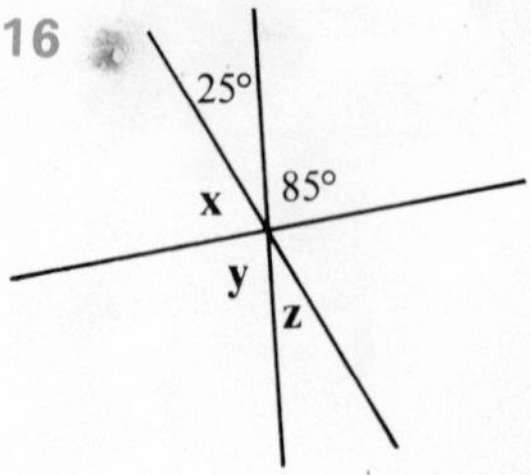
25°
x 85°
y
z

17
a
10° 40°
b c

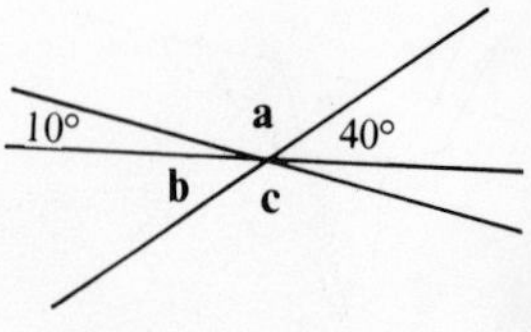

18
i 90° i
j k

19 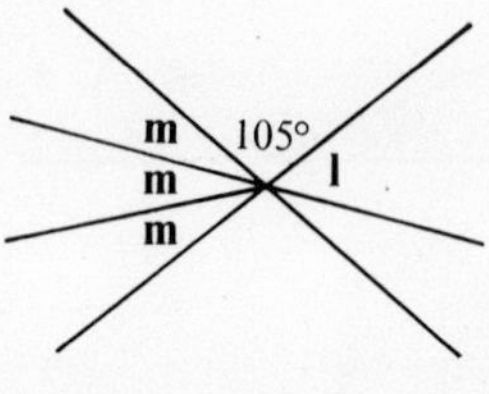
m 105°
m l
m

20
130° t u 75°
z
88°
y x
v 143°
w

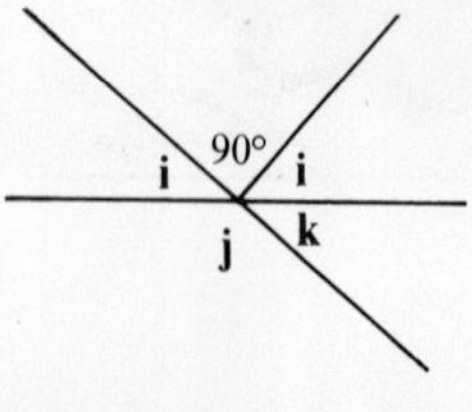

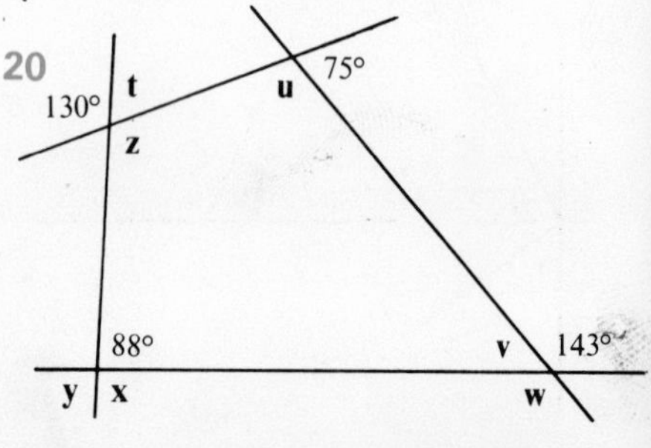

Points and lines

Part 4 Parallel lines

Find the sizes of the lettered angles in these diagrams.

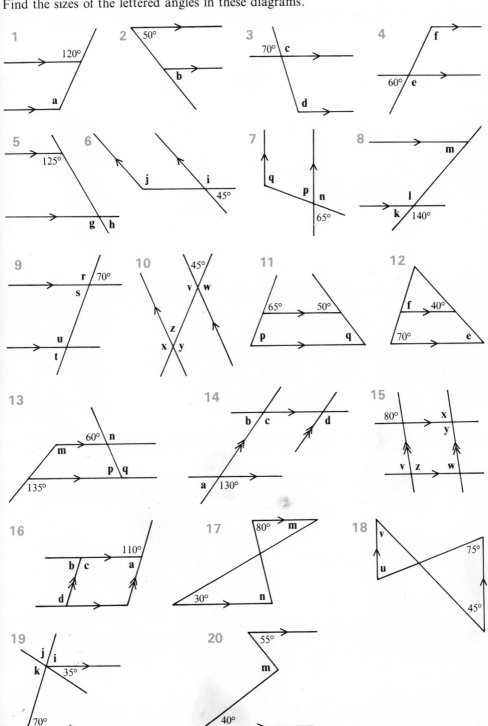

43

Points and lines

Part 5   A mixture

Find the sizes of the lettered angles in these diagrams.
Angles marked with the same letter are equal.

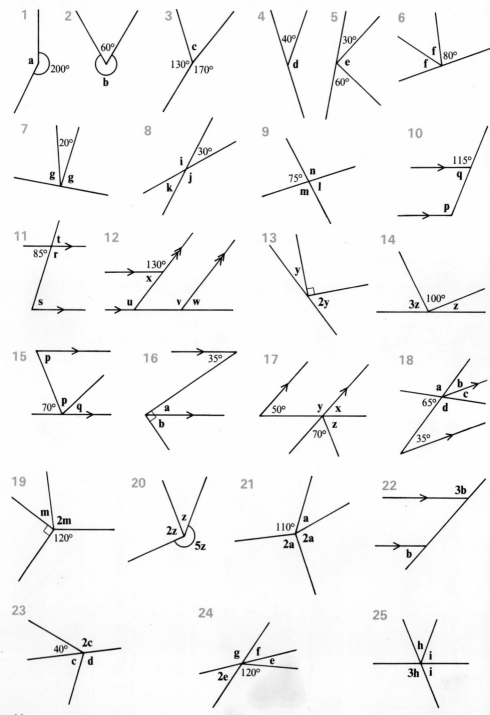

44

Triangles

Part 1 Naming triangles

Triangles can be described by looking (i) at their angles
and (ii) at their sides.

Look at the angles of these three triangles.

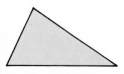 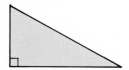 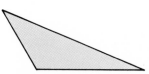

An **acute-angled** triangle
has all its angles
less than 90°.

A **right-angled** triangle
has one angle
equal to 90°.

An **obtuse-angled** triangle
has one angle
greater than 90°.

Look at the sides of these three triangles.

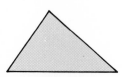

A **scalene** triangle
has all its sides of
different length.

An **isosceles** triangle
has two sides of
equal length.

An **equilateral** triangle
has all its sides of
equal length.

1 Which of these triangles are **acute-angled**, **right-angled** or **obtuse-angled**?

a  b   c  d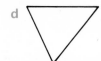

e  f  g h

2 Which of these triangles are **scalene**, **isosceles** or **equilateral**?

a   b 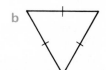 c   d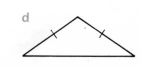

e 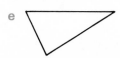 f   g   h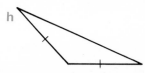

Triangles

3 By looking at the angles and then the sides give each of these triangles *two* descriptions.

For example, this triangle is both **acute-angled** and **isosceles**.

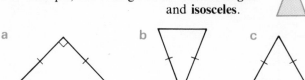

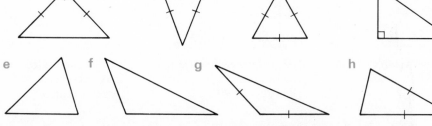

4 On squared paper, draw and label both axes from 0 to 10.
Draw the triangles with these corners. Describe each triangle using *two* words by looking at their angles and their sides.

a $(1,1)(1,2)(4,1)$ b $(1,3)(3,3)(4,6)$ c $(1,6)(2,10)(3,6)$

d $(10,2)(10,5)(8,4)$ e $(5,1)(9,1)(7,4\frac{1}{2})$ f $(4,10)(10,10)(7,9)$

g $(4,9)(5,4)(6,7)$ h $(8,7)(9,6)(10,7)$

Part 2 Angles in triangles

1 Take a piece of paper or card and cut out any triangle.

Label its angles A, B and C.

Tear the triangle along the dotted lines into three pieces and rearrange the angles as shown.

The three angles should make a straight line of 180°.
Hence, $\angle A + \angle B + \angle C = 180°$.

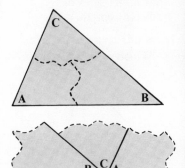

2

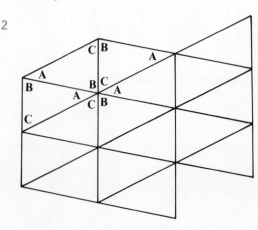

Cut out of paper or card at least 12 triangles all the same size. (It will be quicker to fold the paper several times before cutting.)

Label equal angles A, B and C.

Tessellate the triangles so that they fit together without any gaps as in this diagram.

At any point where six triangles meet, the six angles make a full turn, or three angles make a half turn.

So, for a full turn
$2\angle A + 2\angle B + 2\angle C = 360°$
and, for a half turn
$\angle A + \angle B + \angle C = 180°$.

Triangles

3 Use a protractor to measure the three angles of these two triangles.
For each triangle, add the three angles together.

Use a ruler to draw some more triangles (not too small). Measure their angles
and add them together for each triangle. What do you notice?

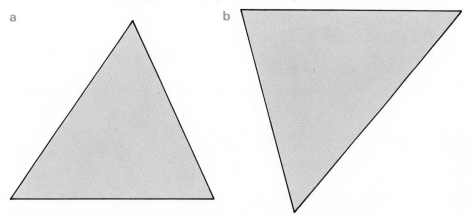

a

b

4 On squared paper, draw and label both axes from 0 to 15.
Draw the four triangles with these corners. Measure their angles with a
protractor and add them together for each triangle.

a (1, 1)(3, 6)(7, 1)   b (1, 14)(1, 8)(8, 14)

c (7, 12)(8, 6)(14, 12)   d (7, 3)(13, 3)(15, 8)

These triangles are *not* drawn accurately. Sketch each one and calculate
the lettered angles.

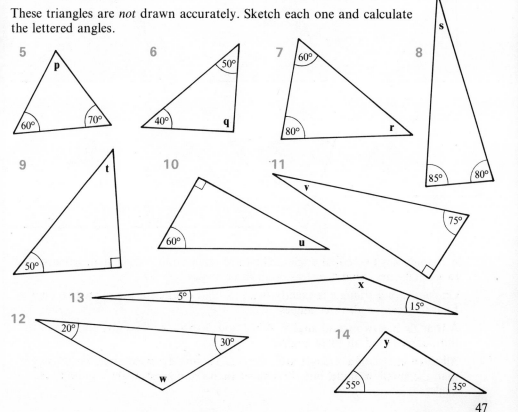

5

p

60°   70°

6

50°

40°   q

7

60°

80°   r

8

s

85°   80°

9

t

50°

10

60°   u

11

v

75°

12

20°   30°

w

13

5°

x

15°

14

y

55°   35°

Triangles

15 If two angles of a triangle are 42° and 12°, find the third angle.

16 If two angles of a triangle are 142° and 22°, calculate the third angle.

17 Find the third angle of a triangle, if the other two are each equal to forty degrees.

18 If all three angles of a triangle are equal, how many degrees is each angle?

19 Is it possible to have a triangle with these three angles 40°, 62°, 76°?

20 If you measure the three angles of a triangle and find they are 54°, 23° and 103°, have you measured them accurately?

21 Two angles of a triangle are 51° and 63°. You measure the third inaccurately as 64°. How many degrees out are you?

Find the value of each letter in these triangles.

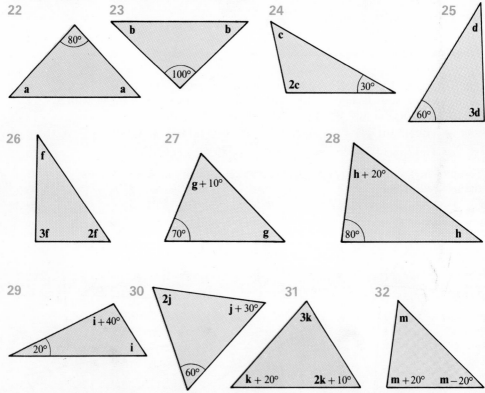

33 A triangle has two equal angles. The third angle is 30° bigger than either of the two equal ones. Find the sizes of all three angles.

34 One angle of a triangle is exactly twice as big as either of the other two angles. Find the sizes of all three angles.

35 A triangle has two equal angles. When added together they give the size of the third angle. Find all three angles.

36 All three angles of a triangle are different. The middle-sized angle is 10° bigger than the smallest angle, but 10° smaller than the biggest angle. Find all three angles.

Triangles

Part 3   Isosceles and equilateral triangles

The word 'isosceles' comes from two Greek
words meaning 'equal legs'.

An isosceles triangle has two equal sides and two
equal angles called **base angles**.

The word 'equilateral' comes from two Latin
words meaning 'equal sides'.

An equilateral triangle has all three sides equal
and all its angles are equal too.

Make a sketch of each triangle and find each of the lettered angles.

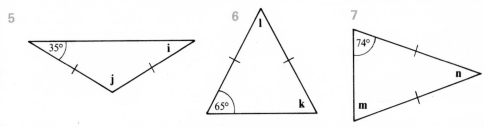

1

2

3

4

5

6

7

These are slightly different.

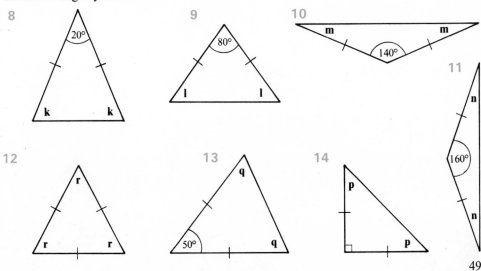

8

9

10

11

12

13

14

49

Triangles

15 Is it possible to have an isosceles triangle with angles of 48°, 48° and 82°?

16 Each base angle of an isosceles triangle is 77°. You measure the third angle with a protractor as 24°. How many degrees out are you?

17 A triangle has one angle of 52° and another angle of 64°. Is the triangle isosceles?

18 If 'equilateral' means 'equal sides', what do you think 'equiangular' means? Is an equilateral triangle also equiangular?

19 The two base angles of an isosceles triangle add up to the third angle. Find the three angles of the triangle.

20 Each base angle of an isosceles triangle is half the third angle. What are the three angles of the triangle?

21 You draw what you think is an equilateral triangle; but two of the angles are each one degree too big. What must be the size of the third angle?

22 Use a protractor to draw two angles each of 40°. Use these angles to draw two entirely different isosceles triangles. Write the sizes of their angles.

Find the value of each letter in the following triangles.

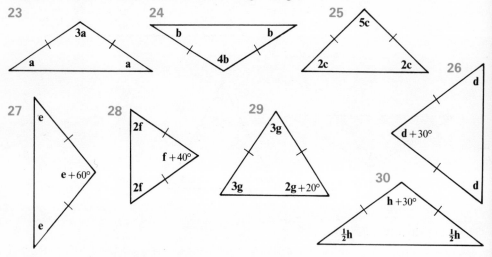

Part 4 Triangles sharing an angle

Triangles in these diagrams have an angle in common.

Find the size of each lettered angle.

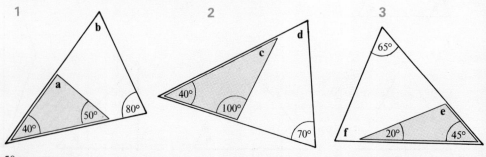

Triangles

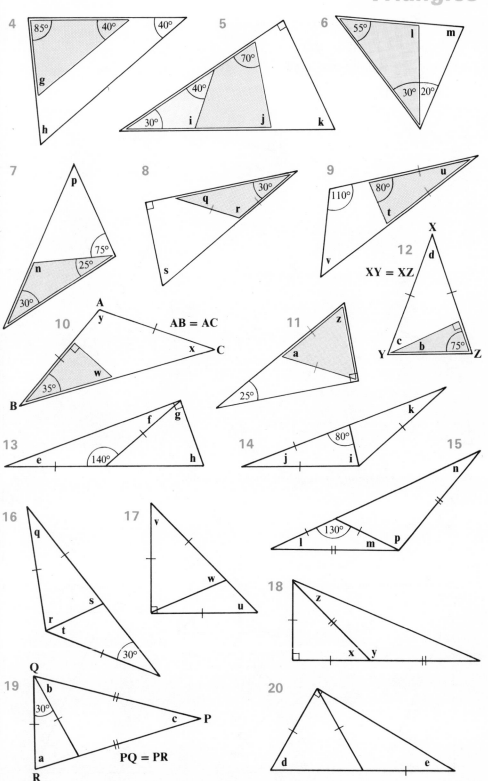

4. 85° 40° 40° g h

5. 70° 40° 30° i j k

6. 55° l m 30° 20°

7. p 75° 25° n 30°

8. q r 30° s

9. u 80° t 110° v

12. X d c b 75° Y Z XY = XZ

10. A y x C w 35° B AB = AC

11. z a 25°

13. f g e 140° h

14. k 80° j i

15. n l 130° m p

16. q s r t 30°

17. v w u

18. z x y

19. Q b 30° c P a R PQ = PR

20. d e

51

Triangles

Part 5   Triangles sharing a side

The triangles in these diagrams have one side in common.
Find the size of each lettered angle.

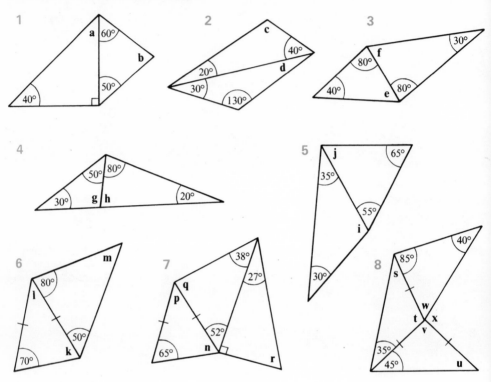

Look for two overlapping triangles in these diagrams.

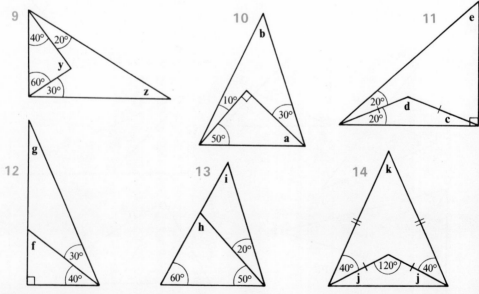

Triangles

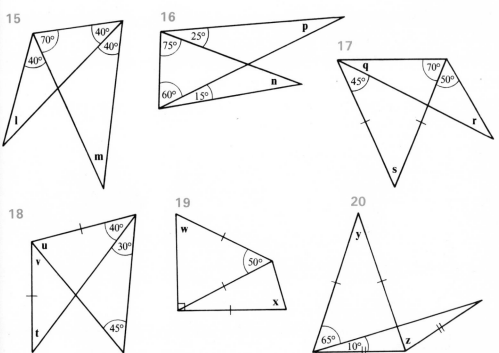

15 70° 40° 40° 40° l m

16 25° 75° 60° 15° p n

17 q 45° 70° 50° s r

18 u v t 40° 30° 45°

19 w 50° x

20 y 65° 10° z

Polygons

Part 1   Quadrilaterals

1   Match each of these nine quadrilaterals with its name from the list.
For example, shape A is a square, so copy the shape and label it 'a square'.

Square	Rectangle	Rhombus	Kite
Parallelogram	Trapezium	Isosceles trapezium	Convex quadrilateral
Concave or re-entrant quadrilateral			

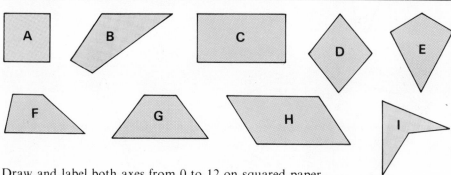

2   Draw and label both axes from 0 to 12 on squared paper.
Plot these sets of four points and join them in the order given to make quadrilaterals.
Name each quadrilateral.

a $(1, 12), (2, 10), (6, 10), (5, 12)$ b $(7, 11), (8, 12), (9, 11), (8, 8)$

c $(11, 12), (12, 10), (11, 8), (10, 10)$ d $(10, 8), (12, 6), (10, 4), (8, 6)$

e $(10, 1), (9, 2), (11, 4), (12, 3)$ f $(6, 0), (4, 1), (5, 3), (7, 2)$

g $(8, 2), (7, 4), (8, 5), (9, 3)$ h $(2, 1), (4, 2), (0, 2), (1, 1)$

i $(5, 7), (6, 9), (7, 9), (8, 7)$ j $(3, 5), (5, 6), (7, 5), (5, 4)$

k $(3, 6), (4, 7), (1, 10), (0, 9)$ l $(0, 6), (1, 5), (2, 3), (2, 6)$

3   Name each of the quadrilaterals which can be found in this diagram.

a   BCEH   b   OBIJ

c   JKLM   d   ADJM

e   ADJN   f   DFKJ

g   DFGJ   h   ABIJ

i   ABHJ   j   ADFK

k   ANJM   l   OBDJ

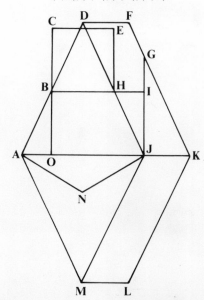

Polygons

4 Copy and complete this table.

	Parallelogram	Rectangle	Square	Rhombus	Kite	Trapezium	Isosceles trapezium
a Are both pairs of opposite angles equal?							
b Are *all* angles equal?							
c Are both pairs of opposite sides parallel?							
d Are both pairs of opposite sides equal?							
e Are *all* sides equal?							
f Are the two diagonals equal?							
g Do the diagonals bisect each other?							
h Do the diagonals intersect at right-angles?							
i How many lines of symmetry are there?							
j What is the order of rotational symmetry?							

5 What name best describes

   a   a rectangle with all its sides the same length

   b   a rhombus with all its angles right-angles

   c   a parallelogram with all its sides equal but *not* all its angles

   d   a parallelogram with all its sides equal *and* all its angles equal

   e   a parallelogram with all its angles equal but *not* all its sides equal

   f   a parallelogram with diagonals of different length intersecting at right-angles

   g   a parallelogram with diagonals of equal length intersecting at right-angles

   h   a kite with all its sides equal?

Polygons

Part 2 Angles in polygons

1 Count the sides of these polygons and so give a name to each.

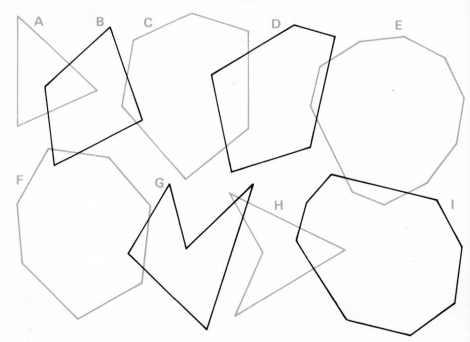

2 a Draw and label the x-axis from 0 to 16 and the y-axis from 0 to 20.
Plot these three sets of points and join them in the order given to make three pentagons.
For each pentagon, use a protractor to measure the five angles and then add the five angles together.
A (4, 1), (11, 1), (16, 6), (9, 9), (1, 7)
B (16, 20), (9, 20), (4, 15), (11, 9), (16, 12)
C (4, 6), (10, 11), (9, 17), (2, 20), (1, 13)

b Draw new axes and label them as before.
Plot these sets of points and join them in order to make three hexagons.
For each one, measure the angles and add them together.
D (2, 1), (9, 1), (12, 7), (11, 14), (5, 14), (1, 8)
E (1, 11), (5, 4), (12, 1), (16, 7), (15, 14), (6, 16)
F (1, 17), (5, 9), (10, 9), (16, 13), (16, 19), (8, 20)

c Draw new axes and label them as before.
Plot these points and join them in order to make two heptagons.
For each one, measure the angles and add them together.
G (1, 4), (7, 1), (14, 1), (16, 8), (15, 14), (7, 14), (1, 10)
H (1, 13), (4, 7), (12, 6), (16, 12), (15, 18), (9, 20), (2, 19)

d Draw new axes and label them as before.
Plot these points and join them in order to make two octagons.
For each one, measure the angles and add them together.
I (5, 1), (11, 1), (16, 4), (16, 11), (11, 15), (4, 15), (0, 10), (0, 4)
J (2, 6), (7, 3), (13, 6), (16, 13), (14, 19), (8, 20), (1, 19), (0, 13)

Polygons

3   Here is a list of a number of polygons.

Draw an example of each one in turn (trying *not* to draw a *concave* polygon).

In each polygon, choose one corner and join it to all the other corners.

Count the number of triangles formed.

Use the fact that the angles of each triangle add up to 180° to calculate the sum of the angles of the polygon.

Quadrilateral
Pentagon
Hexagon
Heptagon
Octagon
Nonagon
Decagon
Undecagon
Dodecagon

For example, this nonagon splits into seven triangles, so the sum of its seven angles is $7 \times 180° = 1260°$.

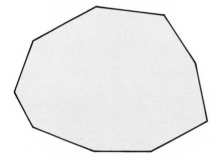 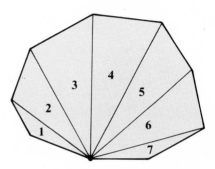

Copy the table below and enter the results.

Complete the row for an icosagon without drawing one.

Can you complete the row for an *n*-sided polygon?

Polygon	Number of sides	Number of triangles	Sum of all angles
Triangle	3	1	$1 \times 180° = 180°$
Quadrilateral	4		
Pentagon	5		
Hexagon	6		
Heptagon	7		
Octagon	8		
Nonagon	9		
Decagon	10		
Undecagon	11		
Dodecagon	12		
Icosagon	20		
n-sided	*n*		

Polygons

4   Count the sides and write the name of each of these polygons. Then calculate
the size of each lettered angle.

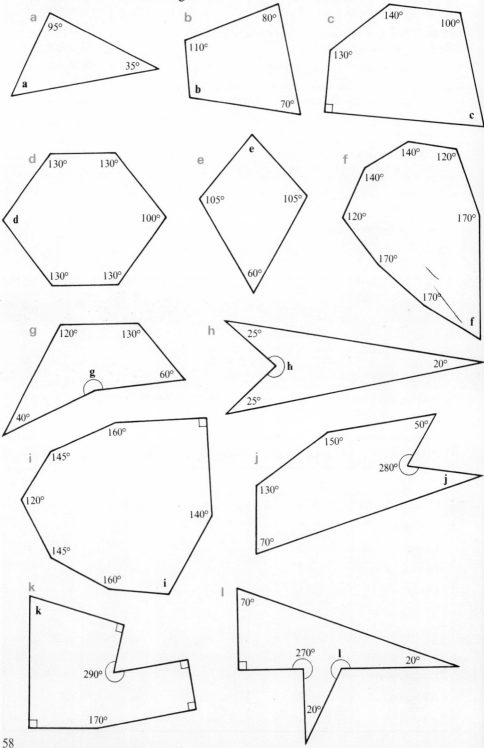

Polygons

5   A pentagon has three angles of 120°, 70° and 130°. If its other two angles are equal, find the size of one of them.

6   A hexagon has three angles of 145°, 105° and 155°. If its other three angles are all equal, what is the size of one of them?

7   A heptagon has angles of 150°, 165°, 145°, 100°, 115° and 95°. What is the size of its other angle?

8   A pentagon has one angle of 80°. If all its other angles are equal, what is the size of one of them?

9   An octagon has six angles of 145° each. If its other two angles are equal, find their size.

10   A dodecagon has nine angles of 160° each. If its other angles are equal, find the size of one of them.

11   A decagon has five angles of 132° each and another three angles of 150° each. Its remaining two angles are equal. What is their size?

12   An octagon has four angles equal to 95° and two angles of 175° and 170° respectively. If its final two angles are equal, what is their size?

Find the value of each letter.

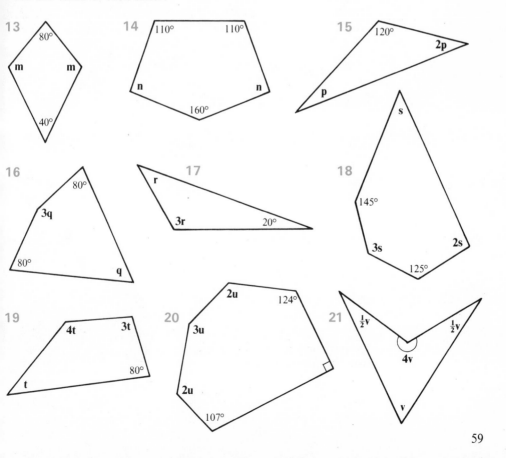

13   80° m m 40°

14   110° 110° n 160° n

15   120° 2p p s

16   80° 3q 80° q

17   r 3r 20°

18   145° 3s 2s 125°

19   4t 3t 80° t

20   2u 124° 3u 2u 107°

21   ½v ½v 4v v

Polygons

22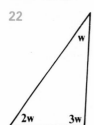

23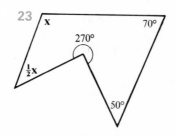

24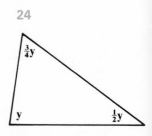

25 One angle of a triangle is 60°. The second angle is 10° bigger than the third angle. Write the sizes of all three angles.

26 Two angles of a quadrilateral are 105° each. The third angle is 30° more than the fourth angle. Write the sizes of all four angles of the quadrilateral.

27 Three angles of a pentagon are 110° each and the fourth angle is 50° more than the fifth angle. Calculate the two unknown angles.

Find the value of each letter.

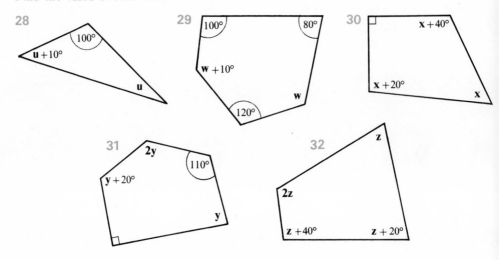

Part 3   Regular polygons

These polygons have all their sides equal and all their angles equal. They are all *regular* polygons.

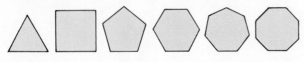

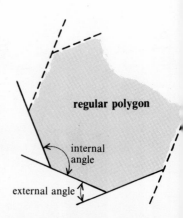

regular polygon

internal angle

external angle

Do not confuse an *internal* angle with an *external* angle.

Polygons

1   Copy this table and use the results from page 57 to complete the third column.
Now complete the other columns for these *regular* polygons.

Regular polygon	Number of sides	Sum of **all** internal angles	Size of **one** internal angle	Size of **one** external angle	Sum of **all** external angles
Triangle	3				
Quadrilateral	4				
Pentagon	5				
Hexagon	6				
Heptagon	7				
Octagon	8				
Nonagon	9				
Decagon	10				
Undecagon	11				
Dodecagon	12				
Icosagon	20				
n-sided	n				

Label axes as shown here and plot a graph of internal angles against the number of sides.

Is it sensible to join the points with a smooth curve?

As the number of sides increases, what value is the internal angle approaching?

As the number of sides increases, what is the name of the shape to which the regular polygon is approximating?

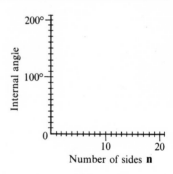

2   There are two methods of drawing regular polygons.

Method 1   Corner by corner

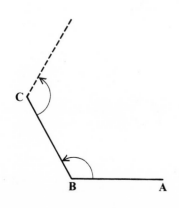

A *sharp* pencil, a ruler and a protractor will be needed.

a   Decide which polygon to draw.

b   Draw side *AB* 5 cm long and at *B* draw an angle of the polygon.

c   Draw side *BC* 5 cm long and at *C* draw another angle of the polygon.

d   Repeat until you arrive back at *A*. You will have to draw *very* accurately to reach *A* *exactly*. The size of the gap that is left will tell you how accurate you have been.

Polygons

Method 2   Using a circumcircle

A pair of compasses will be needed.

a   Decide which polygon to draw.
(A pentagon is shown here.)

b   Draw a circle of radius 5 cm.

c   Split the circle into equal sectors by
dividing the number of sides of the
polygon into 360° and using a protractor:

e.g. for a pentagon, $5\overline{)360}^{\,72}$

so angle α is 72°.

d   Draw the radii of the circle and join their
ends together with straight lines.

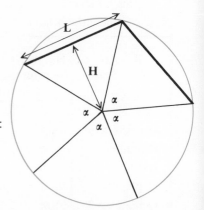

3   **A graphical exercise**

Draw several different types of regular polygon (using method **2** with a radius of
5 cm).

For each one, find
   (i)   angle α
  (ii)   the length of its side L
and (iii)   the area A of the polygon by first measuring side L and height H, then
           multiplying the area of one triangle by the number of triangles in the
           polygon.

Copy this table and complete for each polygon drawn.

Name of polygon						
Number of sides	n					
Angle	$\alpha°$					
Length of one side	L cm					
Area of polygon	A cm²					

Use axes as shown here to draw three graphs:
  (i)   angle α against the number of sides n
 (ii)   the length of a side L against the number of sides n
(iii)   the area A against the number of sides n

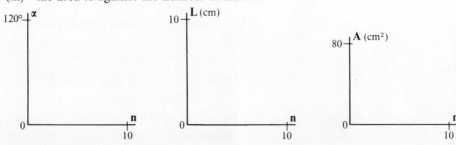

a   Is it sensible to join the points with a smooth curve?
b   As n increases, what value does α approach?
c   As n increases, what value does L approach?
d   As n increases, does the area of the polygon increase or decrease?

e   From the graph, estimate the maximum value or *limit* which the area is approaching.

f   When *n* is very large, to what shape will this regular polygon be approximating?

g   Calculate the value of πr^2 when $\pi = 3.14$ and $r = 5$.
Draw a straight line on your area graph to show this value.

h   Copy and complete this statement:
'As $n \to \infty$, the area of a regular polygon $\to$ the area of ....'

4   Place a pencil on this regular pentagon at corner *A* as shown and rotate it through angle *a*. Slide it to corner *B* and rotate it through angle *b*. Slide it to corner *C* and rotate it through angle *c*.
Repeat at corners *D* and *E*.

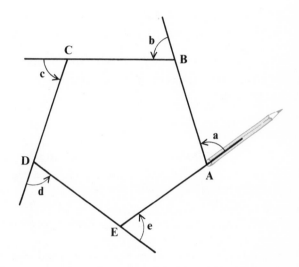

a   How many full turns has the pencil made?

b   What sum do the exterior angles of a regular pentagon add up to?

c   Repeat this method for *any other* polygon—regular or not regular. How many full turns does the pencil rotate?

d   What can be said about the sum of the exterior angles of *any* polygon?

5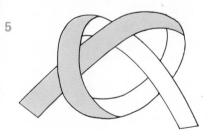

Take a strip of paper about 20 cm long and 2 cm wide.
Tie a simple knot in it as shown and carefully tighten it.
When it is as tight as possible, flatten the knot without crumpling the paper.
Cut away the two ends of the strip.
What regular polygon have you made?

6   a   What other name is given to a regular triangle?

b   What other name is given to a regular quadrilateral?

c   Which regular polygon is used in the design of the fifty-pence piece?

d   Which regular polygon is used in the design of the twenty-pence piece?

e   What shape do bees use when building a honeycomb?

7   Find (i) the sum of all the internal angles
and (ii) the size of each internal angle of a regular polygon which has
    a   8 sides   b   12 sides   c   18 sides   d   25 sides   e   15 sides.

8   Find the size of each external angle of a regular polygon which has
    a   10 sides   b   18 sides   c   40 sides   d   16 sides   e   30 sides.

9   How many sides has a regular polygon if each of its external angles is
    a   36°   b   18°   c   12°   d   20°   e   40°?

Polygons

10 Find (i) the size of an external angle
and (ii) the number of sides
of a regular polygon which has an internal angle of
a 108°   b 150°   c 170°   d 165°   e 156°.

11 A regular polygon has external angles of $x°$ each and internal angles of $4x°$ each.
Find
  a the value of x b the number of sides of the regular polygon.

12 A regular polygon has each external angle of $y°$ and each internal angle of $2y°$.
Find
  a the value of y b the number of sides of the polygon.

13 A regular polygon has external angles of $z°$ each and internal angles of $9z°$ each.
Find
  a the value of z b the number of sides of the polygon.

14 A regular polygon has an external angle of $x°$ and an internal angle of $x + 140°$.
Find
  a the value of x b the number of sides of the polygon.

15 A polygon has an external angle of $y°$ and an internal angle of $y + 100°$.
Find
  a the value of y b the number of sides of the polygon, if it is regular.

16 The external and internal angles of a regular polygon are $z°$ and $z + 36°$
respectively. Find
  a the value of z b the number of sides of the polygon.

17 Each external angle of a regular polygon is $x°$. Find the number of sides n of the
polygon in terms of x.

18 A regular polygon has n sides. Find in terms of n
  a the size of an external angle
  b the size of an internal angle.

19 A regular polygon has n sides. Find in terms of n
  a the number of triangles into which the polygon can be split when one of its
    corners is joined to each other corner
  b the total of all its internal angles
  c the size of each internal angle
  d the size of each external angle.

20 a Show that your answers to **18b** and **19c** are equivalent.
  b Show that your answers to **18a** and **19d** are equivalent.

Revision problems

Find the size of each lettered angle.

Part 1   Triangles and lines

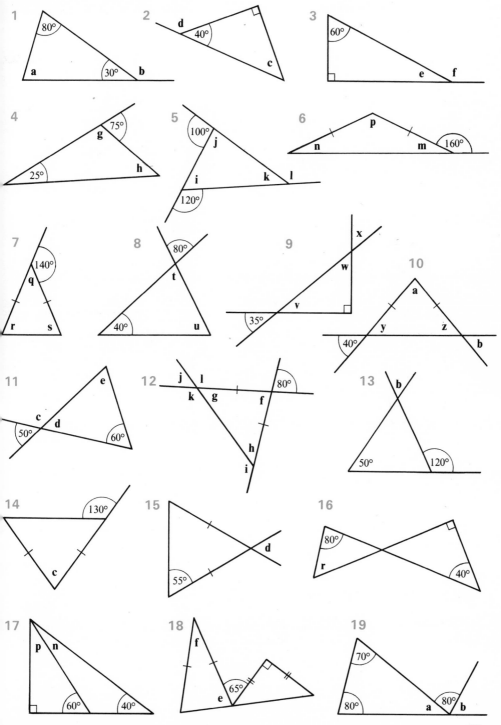

Revision problems

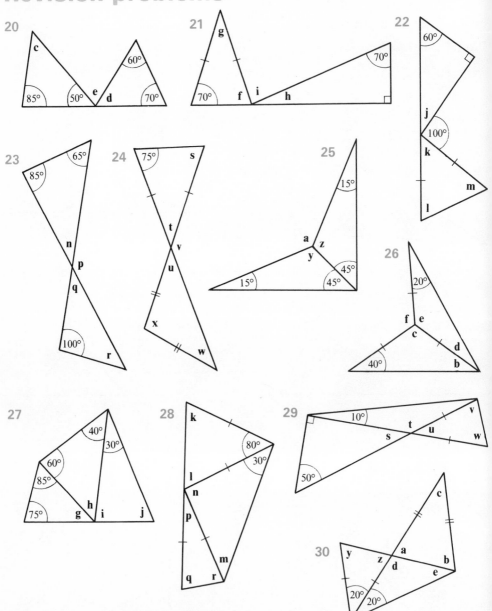

20 c, 85°, 50°, e, d, 60°, 70°

21 g, 70°, f, i, h, 70°

22 60°, j, 100°, k, l, m

23 65°, 85°, n, p, q, 100°, r

24 75°, s, t, v, u, x, w

25 15°, a, z, y, 45°, 15°, 45°

26 20°, f, e, c, d, b, 40°

27 40°, 30°, 60°, 85°, 75°, h, g, i, j

28 k, 80°, 30°, l, n, p, q, r, m

29 10°, v, s, t, u, w, 50°

30 c, y, z, a, d, b, e, 20°, 20°

Part 2   Using parallel lines

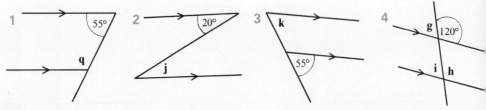

1 55°, q

2 20°, j

3 k, 55°

4 g, 120°, i, h

Revision problems

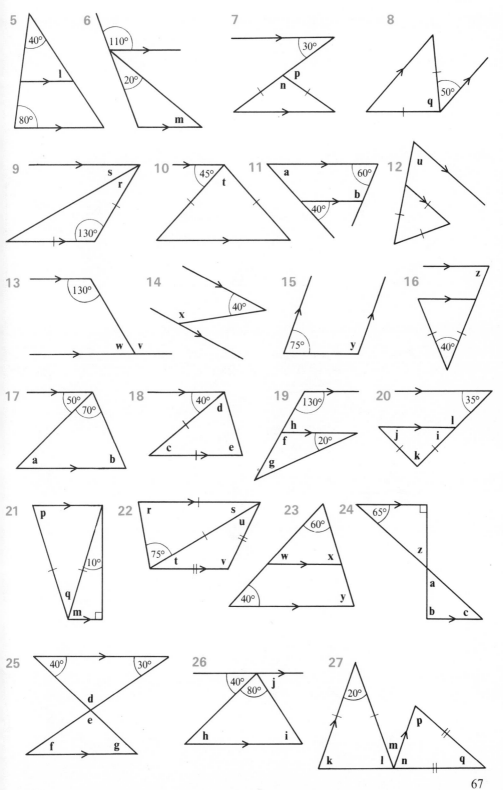

Revision problems

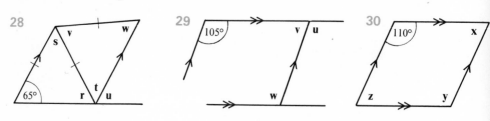

Part 3   A mixture

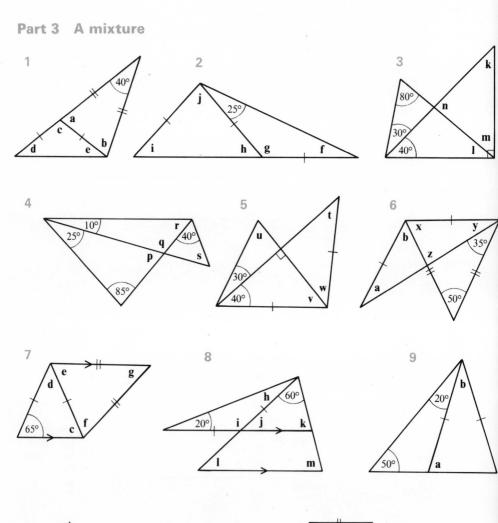

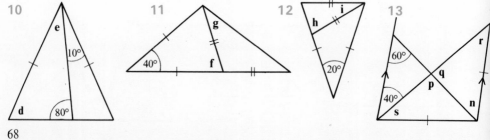

Revision problems

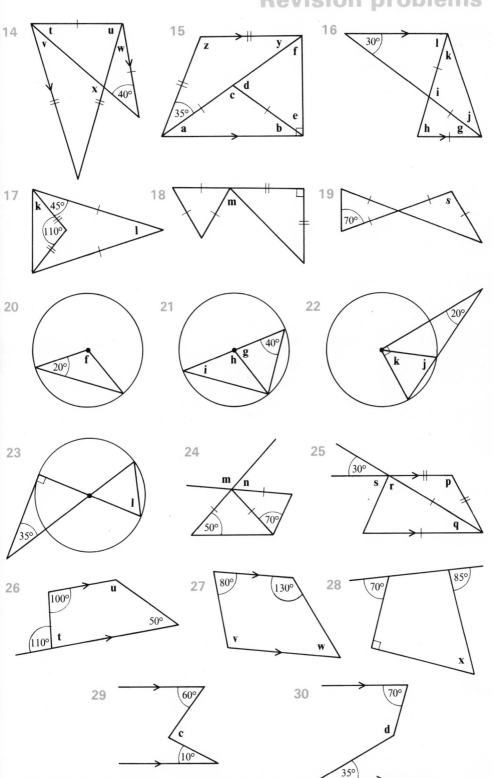

Constructions

Part 1 Triangles

1 A triangle can be constructed if the lengths of its three sides are known.

Construct a triangle with sides 8 cm, 7 cm and 6.5 cm as follows.

Draw the line AB 8 cm long.

With centre A and radius 7 cm, draw the arc X.

With centre B and radius 6.5 cm, draw the arc Y to cut arc X at point C.

Draw triangle ABC.

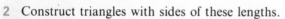

2 Construct triangles with sides of these lengths.

a   6 cm, 5.5 cm, 5 cm
b   7 cm, 5 cm, 4.5 cm
c   8 cm, 7.5 cm, 5 cm
d   5.7 cm, 4.8 cm, 4.3 cm
e   9.2 cm, 6.6 cm, 5.8 cm
f   4.8 cm, 4.3 cm, 3.9 cm

3 Construct triangles with sides as given in this table.

For each triangle, use a protractor to measure the three angles and use a ruler to measure the height of the triangle.

Calculate the area of each triangle to 3 significant figures.

Copy the table and enter the results.

	Lengths of sides cm			Sizes of angles			Height cm	Area cm^2
	AB	AC	BC	$\angle A$	$\angle B$	$\angle C$		
a	7.0	6.5	6.0					
b	8.0	7.5	7.0					
c	6.5	6.0	5.5					
d	8.5	8.5	7.0					
e	9.5	7.5	7.0					
f	6.2	5.8	5.5					
g	9.8	8.6	4.3					
h	8.5	5.0	4.6					

4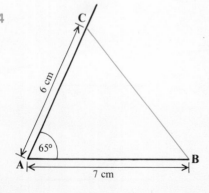

A triangle can be constructed if two sides and the included angle are known.

Construct a triangle having two sides of 7 cm and 6 cm with an angle of 65° between them.

Draw the line AB 7 cm long.

Use a protractor to draw an angle of 65° at A.

Mark point C so that AC is 6 cm.

Draw triangle ABC.

Constructions

5 Construct triangles with sides of these lengths and these included angles.

   a   8 cm, 50°, 5 cm   b   7 cm, 75°, 4 cm

   c   10 cm, 30°, 6 cm   d   8.5 cm, 90°, 5.5 cm

   e   6.4 cm, 110°, 6.4 cm   f   7.2 cm, 135°, 4.2 cm

6 Construct the triangles *ABC* with the sides and included angles given in this table.

For each triangle, use a ruler to measure the third side BC and use a protractor to measure the other two angles.

Measure the height of each triangle and calculate its area to 3 significant figures.

Copy the table and enter the results.

	Lengths of sides cm			Sizes of angles			Height cm	Area cm²
	AB	*AC*	*BC*	∠*A*	∠*B*	∠*C*		
a	6.8	6.2		70°				
b	7.4	6.5		55°				
c	9.8	4.1		82°				
d	6.5	6.0		23°				
e	8.5	5.0		40°				
f	7.5	6.8		100°				
g	5.2	5.2		120°				
h	8.7	4.6		134°				

7 A triangle can be constructed if two angles and the included side are known.

Construct a triangle having angles of 50° and 45° at the ends of a side of 8 cm.

Draw the line *AB* 8 cm long.

Use a protractor to draw an angle of 50° at *A*.

Now use it to draw an angle of 45° at *B*.

C is the point of intersection of these two sides.

Draw triangle *ABC*.

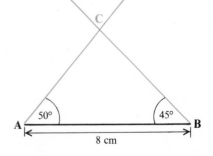

8 Construct triangles with these angles and these included sides.

   a   60°, 9 cm, 50°   b   70°, 8.5 cm, 30°   c   80°, 6 cm, 45°

   d   90°, 6.8 cm, 41°   e   100°, 5.8 cm, 37°   f   124°, 4.7 cm, 28°

Constructions

9   Construct a triangle *ABC* with the angles and included side given in this table.

For each triangle, use a ruler to measure the sides *AC* and *BC* and use a protractor to measure angle *C*.

Measure the height of each triangle and calculate its area to 3 significant figures.

	Lengths of sides cm			Sizes of angles			Height cm	Area cm²
	AB	*AC*	*BC*	∠*A*	∠*B*	∠*C*		
a	8.0			50°	45°			
b	6.5			75°	38°			
c	5.8			27°	71°			
d	4.8			90°	48°			
e	7.1			31°	90°			
f	4.5			48°	100°			
g	6.8			26°	115°			
h	5.9			21°	135°			

Part 2   Bisecting an angle

1   Use a protractor to draw an angle of 60°.

Open some compasses to any radius.

With centre *A*, draw arcs *X* and *Y*.

With centre *X*, draw arc *P*.

With centre *Y* and the same radius, draw an arc to cut *P* at point *B*.

Join *AB*.

Use a protractor to check that the 60° angle has been bisected.

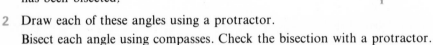

2   Draw each of these angles using a protractor.

Bisect each angle using compasses. Check the bisection with a protractor.

   a   40°   b   50°   c   90°   d   120°   e   140°

A protractor should *not* be used in these next constructions.

3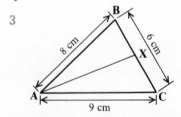

Construct triangle *ABC* with sides of 9 cm, 8 cm and 6 cm.

Construct the bisector of angle *A*, and label the point *X* where it intersects the side *BC*.

Measure and write the lengths *BX* and *CX*.

4   Construct triangle *PQR* with sides of 6 cm, 9 cm and 12 cm.

Construct the bisector of angle *P* and label the point *Y* where it intersects the side *QR*.

Measure and write the lengths *QY* and *RY*.

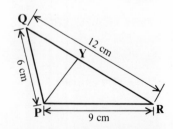

Constructions

5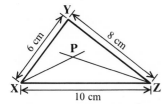

Construct triangle XYZ with sides of 6 cm, 8 cm and 10 cm.

Construct the bisectors of angles X and Z.

Label their point of intersection P.

Measure and write the distance PY.

6 Construct triangle LMN with sides $LM = 10.5$ cm, $LN = 9$ cm and $MN = 7$ cm. Construct the bisectors of all three angles L, M and N. What do you notice? Label their point of intersection A.

Measure and write the distances AL, AM and AN.

7 Draw a triangle of *any* size (but not too small) and bisect its three angles. What do you notice about these three angle bisectors?

Part 3   Bisecting a line

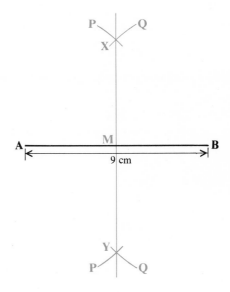

1 Use a ruler to draw a line AB 9 cm long.

Use compasses with any radius and with centre A, draw arcs P.

With centre B and the same radius, draw arcs Q.

Join the points of intersection X and Y and label the point M.

Use a ruler to check that M is the midpoint of AB.

Use a protractor to check that XY is perpendicular to AB.

XY is called the **perpendicular bisector** or **mediator** of AB.

2 Draw lines with these given lengths using a ruler.

Construct the perpendicular bisector (mediator) of each line.

Check the construction by using a ruler and protractor.

a   8 cm   b   6 cm   c   4 cm   d   5 cm   e   7 cm

3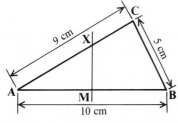

Construct the triangle ABC with sides 10 cm, 9 cm and 5 cm long.

Construct the perpendicular bisector (mediator) of side AB and label the point X where it intersects AC.

Measure and write the lengths AX and CX.

Constructions

4   Construct the triangle *PQR* with sides 8 cm,
    8 cm and 6 cm long.

    Construct the perpendicular bisector
    (mediator) of side *PQ* and label the point
    at which *Y* intersects *QR*.

    Measure and write the lengths *RY* and *QY*.

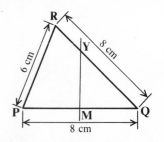

5

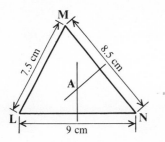

Construct the triangle *LMN* with sides
9 cm, 8.5 cm and 7.5 cm long.

Construct the perpendicular bisectors
(mediators) of sides *LN* and *MN* and
label their point of intersection *A*.

Measure and write the lengths *LA*, *MA*
and *NA*.

6   Construct the triangle *XYZ* with sides of 11 cm, 10 cm and 8 cm.

    Construct the three perpendicular bisectors (mediators) of its three sides.

    What do you notice?

    Label their point of intersection *I*.

    Measure and write the distances *XI*, *YI* and *ZI*.

7   Draw a triangle of *any* size (but not too small) and construct the three
    perpendicular bisectors (mediators) of its three sides. What do you notice?

Part 4   Constructing a perpendicular at a point on a line

1   Draw a line *AB* of any length.
    Mark a point *X* on it.

    With centre *X*, use compasses to
    draw two arcs *S* and *T*.

    Open the compasses further and
    with centre *S* draw arc *P*.

    With the same radius and with
    centre *T*, draw arc *Q*.

    Label the point of intersection *Y*
    and join *XY*.

    Use a protractor to check that *XY*
    is perpendicular to *AB*.

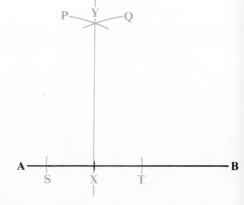

2

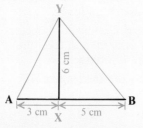

Draw the line *AB* 8 cm long and mark
point *X* such that *AX* = 3 cm.

Construct the perpendicular *XY* and mark
point *Y* such that *XY* = 6 cm.

Draw the triangle *ABY*.

Measure and write the lengths *AY* and *BY*.

Constructions

3

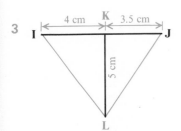

Draw the line *IJ* 7.5 cm long and mark point *K* where *KJ* = 3.5 cm.

Construct the perpendicular *KL* and mark the point *L* where *KL* = 5 cm.

Draw the triangle *IJL*.

Measure and write the lengths *IL* and *JL*.

4 Draw a line *PQ* 10 cm long and mark point *X* 3 cm from *P* and point *M* 3 cm from *Q*.

Construct the perpendicular *XY* and mark point *Y* where *XY* = 6 cm.

Construct the perpendicular *MN* and mark point *N* where *MN* = 6 cm.

Join *YN* and mark point *O* where it intersects *PQ*.

Measure and write the lengths *YN* and *OP*.

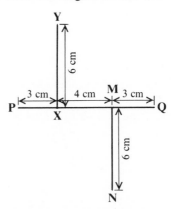

5

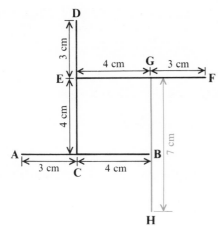

Draw the line *AB* 7 cm long and mark point *C* where *AC* = 3 cm.

Construct the line *DC* perpendicular to *AB* and 7 cm long.

Mark point *E* on *DC* where *DE* = 3 cm.

Construct the line *EF* perpendicular to *DC* and 7 cm long.

Mark point *G* on *EF* where *FG* = 3 cm.

Construct the line *GH* perpendicular to *EF* and 7 cm long.

Does *B* lie on *GH*?

Measure and write the distances between
  a *A* and *F*   b *D* and *H*.

Part 5 Constructing a perpendicular to a line from a point off the line

1 Draw a line *AB* of any length.

Mark a point *X* not on the line.

With centre *X*, use compasses to draw an arc to intersect the line at *S* and *T*.

With centre *S*, draw the arc *P*.

With centre *T* and the same radius, draw the arc *Q* to cut arc *P* at point *Y*.

Join *XY*.

Use a protractor to check that *XY* is perpendicular to *AB*.

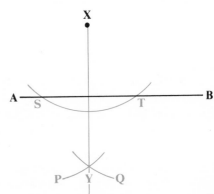

Constructions

2

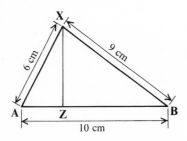

Construct triangle *ABX* with sides of 10 cm, 9 cm and 6 cm.

Construct a perpendicular from *X* to meet *AB* at point *Z*.

Measure and write the lengths *AZ* and *XZ*.

The perpendicular *XZ* is one of the three *altitudes* of triangle *ABX*.

3 Construct triangle *PQR* with sides of 8 cm, 8 cm and 7 cm.

Construct the altitude from *R* to *PQ* to meet *PQ* at *S*.

Measure and write the lengths *PS* and *RS*.

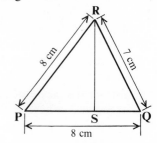

4

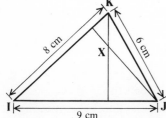

Construct triangle *IJK* with sides of 9 cm, 8 cm and 6 cm.

Construct the altitude from *K* to *IJ*.

Construct the altitude from *J* to *IK*.

Label their point of intersection *X*.

Measure and write the distance *IX*.

5 Construct triangle *XYZ* with *XY* = 6 cm, *XZ* = 5.5 cm and *YZ* = 4 cm.

Construct the three altitudes of the triangle: one from *Z* to *XY*, another from *X* to *YZ* and the third from *Y* to *XZ*.

What do you notice? Label their point of intersection *O*.

Measure and write the lengths *OX*, *OY* and *OZ*.

6 Draw *any* triangle (not too small). Construct the three altitudes of the triangle. What do you notice?

Part 6 Angles of 60°, 30°, 45° etc.

1 Construct an angle of 60° without using a protractor, as follows.

Draw a line *AB*.

With centre *A*, draw an arc *P*, cutting line *AB* at *C*.

With centre *C* and the *same* radius, draw an arc *Q*, cutting arc *P* at point *D*.

Join *AD*.

Use a protractor to check that angle *DAB* is 60°.

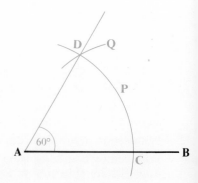

2 Construct an angle of 30° by
  a constructing a 60° angle as above and
  b bisecting it, using the method of Part **2**.

Constructions

3 Construct an angle of 15° by
   a   constructing a 60° angle and   b   bisecting it *twice*.

4 Construct an angle of 45° by
   a   constructing a 90° angle as in Part **4** and   b   bisecting it.

5 Construct an angle of $22\frac{1}{2}°$ by
   a   constructing a 90° angle and   b   bisecting it *twice*.

6

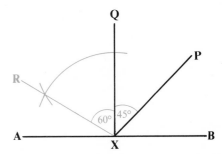

Construct an angle of 105° by adding 45° to 60° as follows.
On line AB, construct a right angle at X.
PX bisects this angle to give $P\widehat{X}Q = 45°$.
On line XQ, construct a 60° angle, where $Q\widehat{X}R = 60°$.
Then, $P\widehat{X}R = 45° + 60° = 105°$.

7 By adding or subtracting two angles, construct these angles without using a protractor.
   a   120°   b   135°   c   75°   d $67\frac{1}{2}°$ e   150°   f   165°

Construct these polygons using ruler and compasses only.
Do *not* rub out your construction lines.
Write the lengths of the sides labelled x.

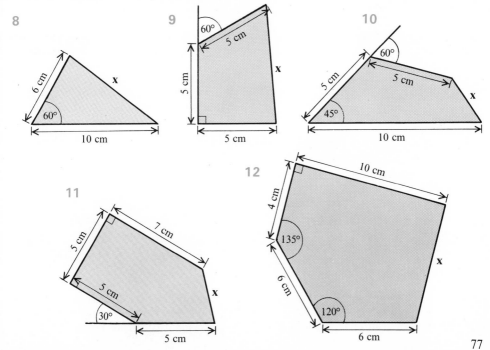

Constructions

Part 7   Incircles and circumcircles

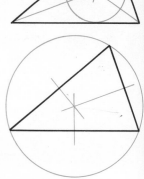

The **incircle** of a triangle is that which is drawn inside the triangle so that it touches the three sides of the triangle. Its centre (the **incentre**) is the point of intersection of the three angle bisectors of the triangle.

The **circumcircle** of a triangle is that which is drawn outside the triangle so that it passes through the three corners of the triangle.

Its centre (the **circumcentre**) is the point of intersection of the three perpendicular bisectors (or mediators) of the triangle.

1   Construct each of these triangles and then construct their incircles. Measure the radius of each incircle.

   a   10 cm, 9 cm, 8 cm   b   9 cm, 8 cm, 7.5 cm

   c   11 cm, 8 cm, 7 cm   d   10 cm, 8 cm, 5 cm

   e   10 cm, 8 cm, 6 cm   f   11 cm, 7 cm, 6.5 cm

2   Construct these triangles again and then construct their circumcircles. Measure the radius of each circumcircle.

3   Three trees are growing so that the distances between them are 11.5 metres, 9.5 metres and 6 metres. A goat is to be tethered to a stake by a rope so that it can just reach each tree.
How long should the rope be?

4

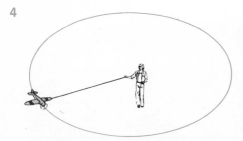

A boy has a model aeroplane which flies in a circle on the end of a horizontal wire. The field in which he flies it has three telegraph poles 55 m, 45 m and 40 m apart at the corners of a triangle. What is the longest length of wire he can use without his aeroplane hitting any of the three poles?
(Use a scale of 1 cm for 5 m.)

5   A child's toy is made from a box having a triangular cross-section with sides 24 cm, 20 cm and 18 cm long, into which a solid cylinder will just fit.
What is the radius of this cylinder? (Use a scale of 1 cm for 2 cm.)

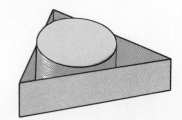

6   When a fair arrives in a town, a children's roundabout is allocated a triangular plot of land having edges 14 metres, 12 metres and 11 metres long.
What is the radius of the largest roundabout which will fit on this plot?

Constructions

Part 8   General problems

Unless a diagram is already provided, draw a rough sketch first so that you have some idea of the shape of the required drawing.

Do *not* rub out any construction lines.

1   Construct a triangle with sides of 6 cm, 5.5 cm and 4 cm.
Label the smallest angle A and construct its bisector.
Mark the point X where this bisector cuts the opposite side.
Measure the length AX.

2   Construct the isosceles triangle ABC with sides $AB = AC = 7$ cm and $BC = 4$ cm.
Construct the bisector of angle B and let it cut AC at X.
Measure the length AX.

3   Construct an equilateral triangle of side 6 cm.
Construct the altitude from any corner to the opposite side.
Measure the length of this altitude.

4   Construct the triangle PQR where $\angle P = 45°$, $PR = 8$ cm and $\angle R = 60°$.
Construct the altitude from Q to PR and measure its length.

5   Construct triangle XYZ where $\angle Y = 90°$, $YZ = 7$ cm and $\angle Z = 60°$.
Bisect any two angles and let these bisectors meet at point P.
Measure the distance PY.

6   The diagonals of a square bisect each other at right-angles.
Construct a square with diagonals 8 cm long.
Measure the length of side of the square.

7   The diagonals of a rhombus bisect each other at right-angles.
Construct a rhombus with diagonals of 9 cm and 6 cm.
Measure the length of side of the rhombus.

8   Another rhombus has diagonals 10 cm and 5 cm long.
Construct the rhombus and measure the length of its sides.

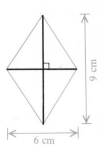

9

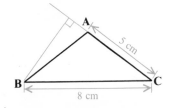

Construct an isosceles triangle ABC with $AB = AC = 5$ cm and $BC = 8$ cm.
Construct the altitude from B to AC, noting that AC will need to be extended as shown.
Measure the length of this altitude.

10   Construct a triangle XYZ with $XY = 5$ cm, $\angle Y = 120°$ and $YZ = 4$ cm.
Construct the altitude from Z to XY and measure its length.

11   Draw a circle of radius 4 cm.
Draw a chord AB of this circle 5 cm long and label its ends.
Construct the perpendicular bisector of this chord.
Draw another chord AC 4 cm long and label the end C.
Construct its perpendicular bisector.
At what point do these two perpendicular bisectors intersect?

Constructions

12 Construct a parallelogram with sides of
4 cm and 7 cm, containing an angle of 45°
between them.
Measure the lengths of the two diagonals
of the parallelogram.

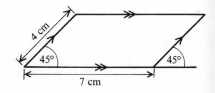

13

Construct a parallelogram with one
side of 8 cm at 60° to a diagonal of
4 cm.
Measure the length of the other
sides of the parallelogram.

14 An isosceles triangle *ABC* has *AB* = *AC* and *BC* = 6 cm.
The altitude from *A* to *BC* is 8 cm.
Construct the triangle and then construct the altitude from *B* to *AC*.
Measure the length of this altitude.

15 Construct an equilateral triangle *LMN* of side 6 cm.
Construct the bisector of angle *L* so that it meets *MN* at *X*.
Construct the perpendicular bisector of *LX* so that it cuts *LM* at *Y* and
LN at *Z*.
Measure *YZ*.

Angles in circles

Introduction

Theorem 1

a Draw a circle (radius 5 cm) and mark two points *A* and *B* on its circumference.

Join *A* and *B* to a point P_1 on the circumference.

Use a protractor to measure angle AP_1B.

Join *A* and *B* to a point P_2 and measure angle AP_2B.

Repeat with points P_3 and P_4 and measure angles AP_3B and AP_4B.

What do you notice about the results?

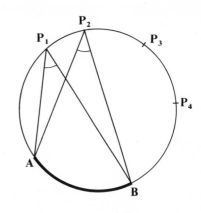

b Still use a circle of radius 5 cm but repeat with the points *A* and *B* further apart as in this diagram.

Measure angles AP_1B and AP_2B.

Do you reach the same conclusion?

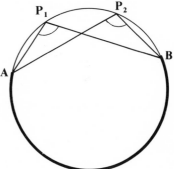

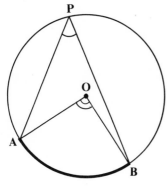

Theorem 2

a Draw a circle (radius 5 cm) and mark two points *A* and *B* on the circumference as shown.

Use a protractor to measure the angle *AOB* at the centre and the angle *APB* at the circumference.

Then repeat with different positions of points *A* and *B* on different circles.

What conclusion do you come to about the sizes of angles *AOB* and *APB*?

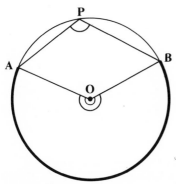

b Repeat with *A* and *B* further apart as in this diagram.

Measure angles *AOB* and *APB*.

Do you reach the same conclusion?

Angles in circles

Theorem 3 (A special case of Theorem 2)

Draw a circle (radius 5 cm). Draw any diameter and label its ends A and B.

Choose any point P_1 and measure angle AP_1B.

Choose any point P_2 and measure angle AP_2B.

Repeat for a point P_3.

What do you notice about the results?

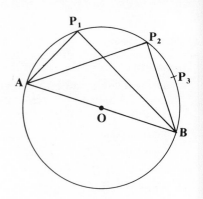

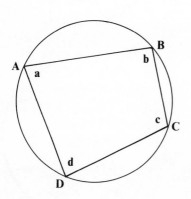

Theorem 4 (An extension of Theorem 2)

Draw a circle (radius 5 cm) and take any four points A, B, C and D on its circumference.

Join them to make a **cyclic** quadrilateral.

Measure the four angles a, b, c and d.

Calculate $a + c$ and $b + d$.

Repeat with another circle and another cyclic quadrilateral.

What conclusions do you reach about the opposite pairs of angles in a cyclic quadrilateral?

Theorem 5

Draw a circle (radius 5 cm) and any radius OP_1.

Draw at P_1 the tangent QR as shown and measure the angles QP_1O and RP_1O.

Repeat for any other point P_2 on the circle.

What do you conclude about the angles you have measured?

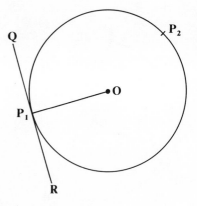

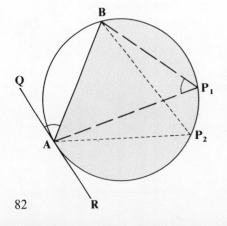

Theorem 6

Draw a circle (radius 5 cm) and a chord AB.

At point A, draw the tangent QR.

Measure angle BAQ.

Join A and B to any point P_1 on the circumference as shown. Measure angle AP_1B.

Repeat by joining A and B to another point P_2 and measure angle AP_2B.

What do you notice about the angles AP_1B and AP_2B compared to angle BAQ?

Angles in circles

Summary of the six theorems

1 Angles standing on the same arc of a circle are equal.

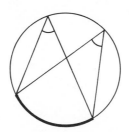 or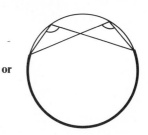

2 The angle which an arc subtends at the centre of a circle is TWICE that which it subtends at the circumference.

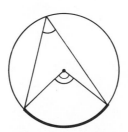 or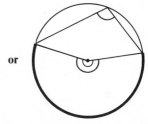

3 The angle in a semicircle is a right angle.

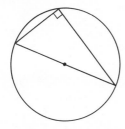

4 The opposite angles of a cyclic quadrilateral add up to 180°.

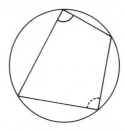

5 The angle between a tangent and a radius is a right angle.

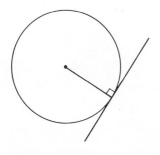

6 The angle between a tangent and a chord equals the angle in the opposite segment.

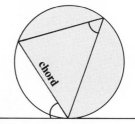

chord

tangent

Angles in circles

Part 1   Angles on the same arc

Calculate the size of each lettered angle.

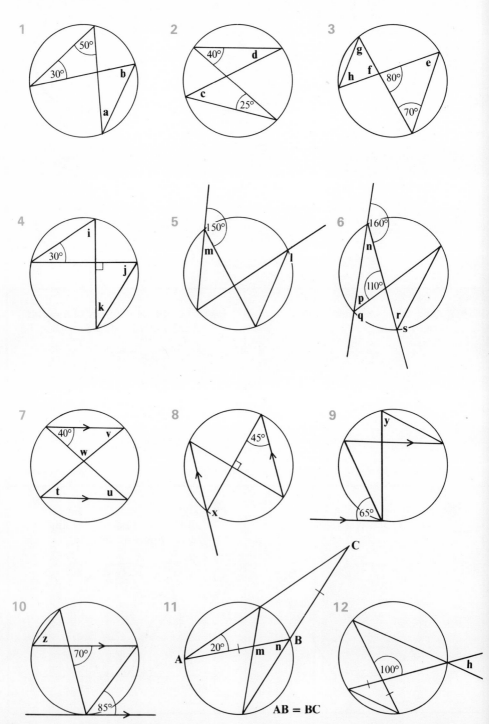

Angles in circles

Part 2 Angles at the centre and at the circumference

Calculate the size of each lettered angle.

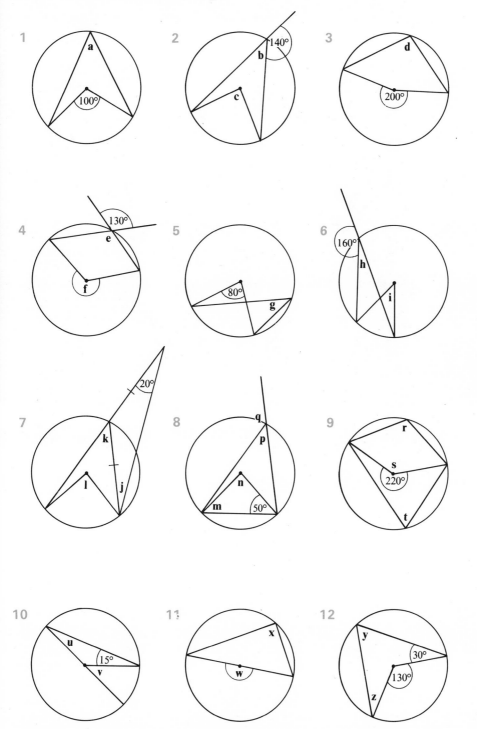

85

Angles in circles

Part 3   Angles in a semicircle

Calculate the size of each lettered angle.

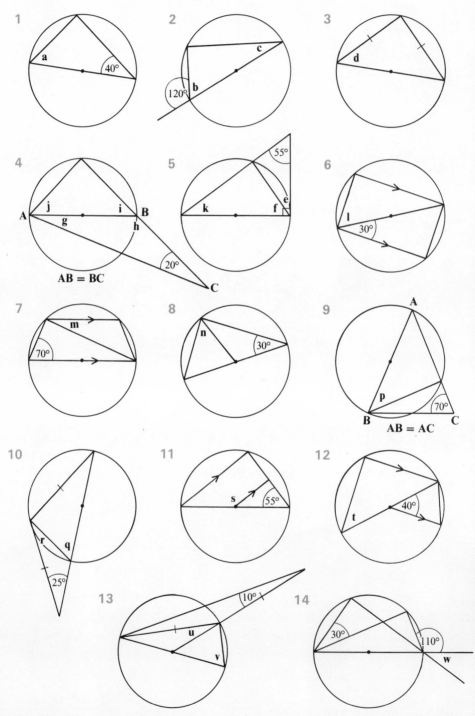

Angles in circles

Part 4 Angles in cyclic quadrilaterals

Calculate the size of each lettered angle.

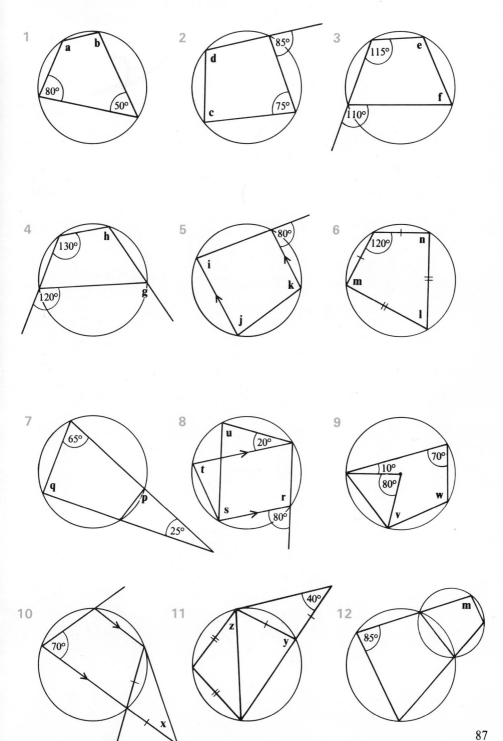

Angles in circles

Part 5   Angles between a tangent and a radius

Calculate the size of each lettered angle.

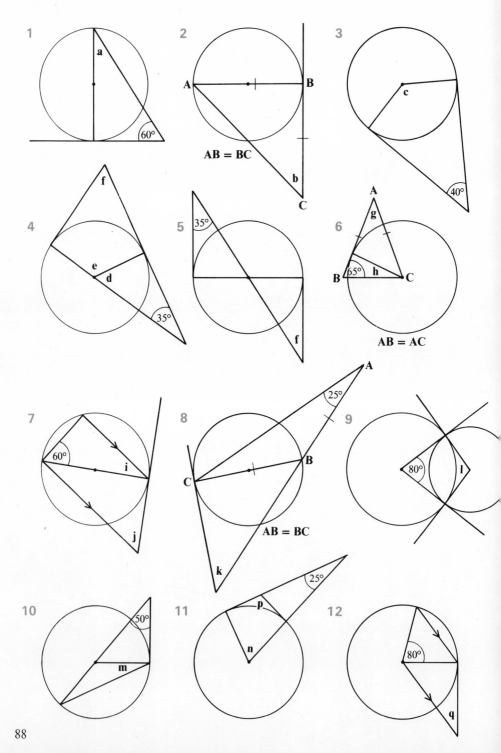

Angles in circles

Part 6   Angles in the opposite segment

Calculate the size of each lettered angle.

1   Introduction

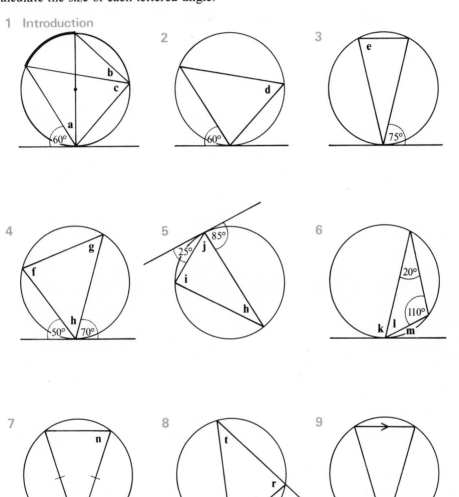

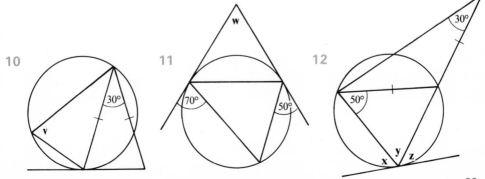

Angles in circles

Part 7   A mixture

Calculate the value of each lettered angle.

Where marked, O is the centre of the circle and T is the point at which a tangent touches the circle.

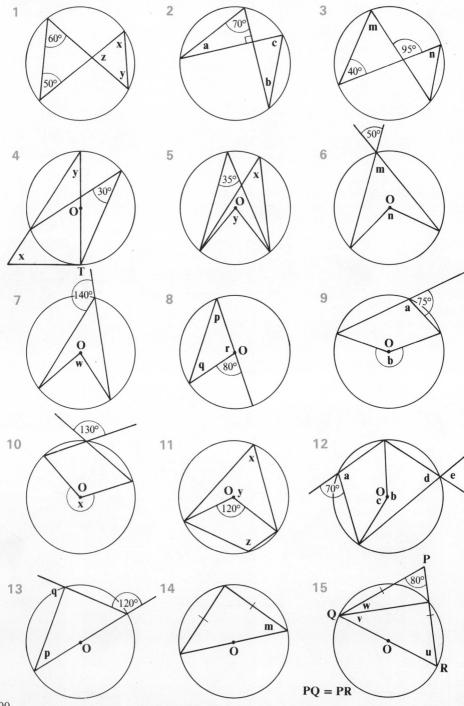

Angles in circles

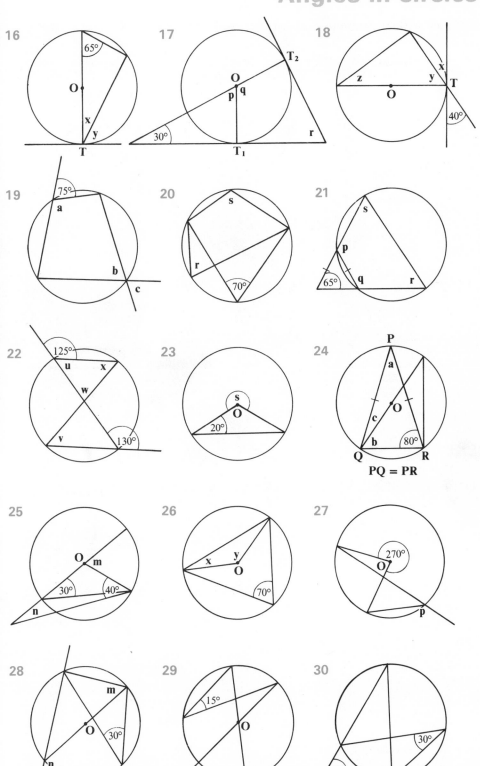

Angles in circles

For each of these diagrams, find the angle y in terms of angle x.

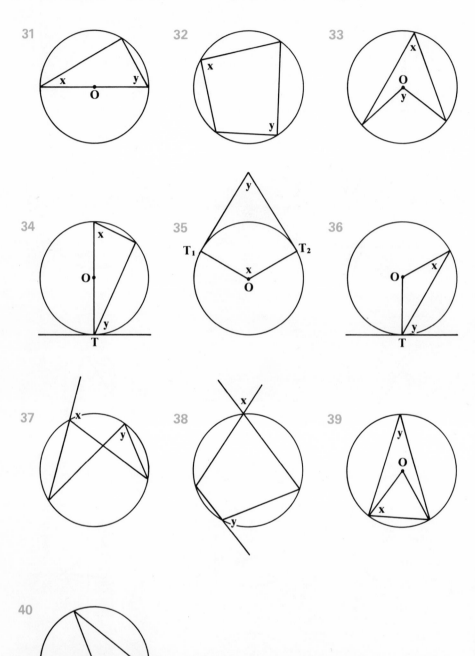

Trigonometry

Tangents

Introduction

1 Angle A = 72°

Draw the right-angled triangle ABC accurately using a ruler and protractor, so that angle $A = 72°$ and $AB = 2$ cm.

Measure the length of BC.

How many times longer is BC than AB?

Copy this table and enter the results in the first row.

AB (cm)	BC (cm)	How many times longer?
2		
3		
4		
2.5		
3.5		

Draw a larger triangle ABC with $AB = 3$ cm but keep angle $A = 72°$.

Measure BC, find how many times longer BC is than AB and enter the results in the second row of the table.

Repeat with $AB = 4$ cm, 2.5 cm and 3.5 cm. Enter the results each time.

2 Angle A = 64°

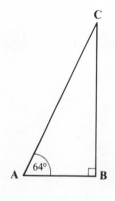

Draw the right-angled triangle ABC accurately using a ruler and protractor so that angle $A = 64°$ and $AB = 2$ cm.

Measure the length of BC.

How many times longer is BC than AB?

Copy this table and enter the results in the first row.

AB (cm)	BC (cm)	How many times longer?
2		
3		
4		
2.5		
3.5		

Draw a larger triangle ABC with $AB = 3$ cm but keep angle $A = 64°$.

Measure BC, find how many times it is longer than AB and enter the results in the second row of the table.

Repeat with $AB = 4$ cm, 2.5 cm and 3.5 cm. Enter the results each time.

Tangents

3   Angle A = 56°

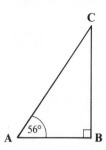

Draw the right-angled triangle *ABC* with angle *A* = 56° and *AB* = 2 cm.

Measure *BC* and find how many times longer it is than *AB*.

Copy this table and enter the results in the first row.

AB (cm)	BC (cm)	How many times longer?
2		
3		
4		

Draw two more triangles with angle *A* = 56° taking *AB* = 3 cm and then 4 cm. Enter the results in the table.

4   Angle A = 45°

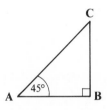

Draw triangle *ABC* with angle *A* = 45° and *AB* = 2 cm.

Repeat with *AB* = 3 cm and 4 cm.

Copy this table and enter all the results.

AB (cm)	BC (cm)	How many times longer?
2		
3		
4		

5   Angle A = 27°

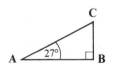

Draw triangle *ABC* with angle *A* = 27°.

Take *AB* = 2 cm, 3 cm and 4 cm.

Copy this table and enter all the results.

AB (cm)	BC (cm)	How many times longer?
2		
3		
4		

6   All the results for the different angles can be brought together into one table. Copy and complete this table.

Angle A	How many times longer BC is than AB or the **tangent** of angle A
72°	
64°	
56°	
45°	
27°	
0°	

Draw a graph of these results using axes as shown here.

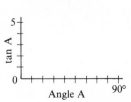

Tangents

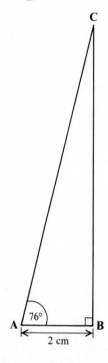

7   Draw this triangle accurately using a ruler and protractor.

Measure the length of BC and so calculate the value of tan 76°. (Check the answer from your graph.)

8   By drawing other right-angled triangles accurately with ruler and protractor, find the values of

a	tan 68°	b	tan 74°	c	tan 56°
d	tan 35°	e	tan 42°	f	tan 70°
g	tan 14°	h	tan 31°	i	tan 60°
j	tan 27°	k	tan 66°	l	tan 33°.

9   For each of these, draw a right-angled triangle with a ruler and then use a protractor to measure the angle which has a tangent of

a	$\frac{7}{10}$	b	$\frac{3}{10}$	c	$\frac{4}{5}$
d	$\frac{2}{5}$	e	$\frac{5}{8}$	f	$1\frac{1}{3}$
g	$2\frac{1}{5}$	h	$1\frac{2}{7}$	i	$\frac{3}{4}$
j	$1\frac{3}{5}$	k	$2\frac{3}{4}$	l	$1\frac{2}{3}$.

10   Copy and memorise the following.

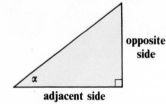

The tangent of angle $\alpha = \dfrac{\text{the length of the opposite side}}{\text{the length of the adjacent side}}$.

In short, $\tan \alpha = \dfrac{\text{opposite}}{\text{adjacent}}$.

Part 1   Finding an angle

Find the angle α in each triangle by calculating its tangent and using tables. The diagrams are *not* to scale.

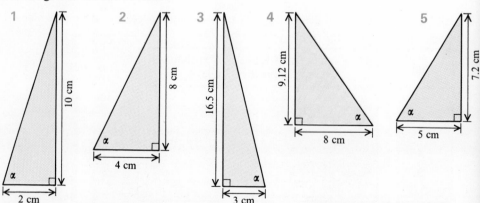

Tangents

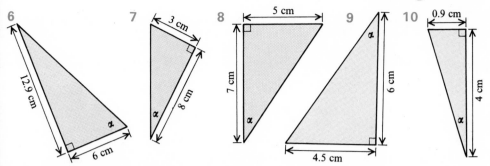

Sketch diagrams to help solve these problems.

11 A funicular railway climbs so steeply up a mountain that for every 5 metres horizontally the train climbs vertically 2 metres. Find the angle to the horizontal at which it is climbing.

12 A ladder leans against a wall so that the foot of the ladder is 2 metres from the wall. If the top of the ladder is 6.4 m above the ground, find the inclination (the angle) of the ladder to the ground.

13 A telegraph pole 10 m high is held by a sloping wire fixed to the top of the pole and also to a point in the ground 4 m from the foot of the pole. Calculate the angle between the wire and the ground.

14 A factory chimney is 35 m tall. If you stand 12 m from its foot, what is the angle of elevation of its top?

15 A cliff is 120 m high. A small fishing boat is 100 m from the bottom of the cliff. Find the angle of elevation of the cliff-top from the boat.

Division by a decimal

Calculate the lettered angles in these triangles to three significant figures.

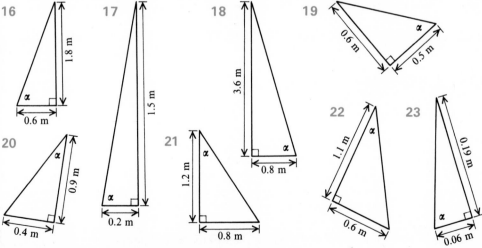

Sketch a diagram to help you solve these problems.

24 A plank of wood leans against a wall so that it reaches 2.9 m up the wall. If its lower end is 0.7 m out from the wall, find the angle that it makes with the ground.

25 A rectangle $ABCD$ has $AB = CD = 1.5$ m and $BC = AD = 0.6$ m. Find the angle between the diagonal BD and the side CD.

Tangents

26 A shepherd walks from his home *H* due north for 0.5 km, and then he walks 2.3 km due east to reach a barn *B*. On what bearing is the barn from the house? Give the answer to the nearest degree.

27 A cone has a height of 0.4 m and a diameter of 1.3 m. Find
   a the semi-vertical angle α of the cone
   b the whole of the angle *A* at the apex.

28 A flag-pole 6.2 m high is held vertical by a sloping wire fixed to its top and to a point on the ground 1.5 m from the foot of the pole. Calculate the inclination of the wire to the ground.

29 A hilltop is 0.75 km above sea-level. What is the angle of elevation of the top from a point at sea-level 1.2 km away from the hill?

30 I leave point *A* and walk 1.1 km due south and then 0.85 km due west to reach point *B*. What is the bearing of *B* from *A* to the nearest degree?

Division by cancelling

Calculate the lettered angles in these triangles.

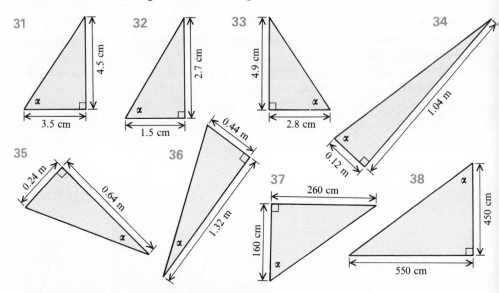

Sketch diagrams to help solve these problems.

39 A kite is flying at a height of 40 m at the end of a straight string. The boy flying it is standing 64 m away from the point vertically below the kite. Find the angle which the string makes with the ground.

40 A banister rail alongside a flight of stairs rises 6.3 m vertically in a horizontal distance of 5.6 m. Find the angle of the rail to the horizontal.

41 Triangle *XYZ* is isosceles with *XY* = *XZ* and *M* the midpoint of *YZ*. If *XM* = 10.5 cm and *YZ* = 15 cm, calculate angle *Y* and hence find the other two angles of the triangle.

42 A tower block of flats casts a shadow 160 m long onto level ground. If the height of the tower block is 220 metres, calculate the altitude of the sun.

Tangents

43 A radio aerial is 120 m high and it casts a shadow 216 m long onto level ground. Calculate the altitude of the sun.

44 A rectangle is 12.6 cm long and 9 cm wide. Calculate both of the angles between its diagonals and the sides.

45 I leave Bough Fell *B* and walk 16.8 km northeast to reach Cumber Fell *C*. I then leave *C* and walk a further 9.6 km southeast to reach Danby Fell *D*. Find

   a   angle *BCD*   b   angle *CBD*

   c   the bearing of *D* from *B* to the nearest degree.

Division by logarithms or calculator

Calculate the lettered angles in these triangles.

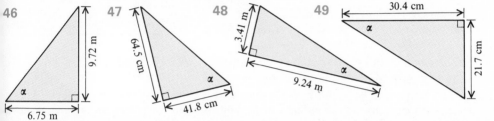

46 9.72 m α 6.75 m

47 64.5 cm α 41.8 cm

48 3.41 m α 9.24 m

49 30.4 cm α 21.7 cm

50 A spire is $45\frac{1}{2}$ m high. Find the angle of elevation of its top from a point $27\frac{1}{2}$ m away on level ground.

51 A fence post 3.2 m high casts a shadow 2.7 m long. Calculate the sun's altitude.

52 A wooden wedge is 367 mm long and its height is 145 mm. Find the angle of the wedge.

Part 2 Finding a side

Find the lengths *x* in these triangles, to three significant figures.

The triangles are *not* drawn to scale.

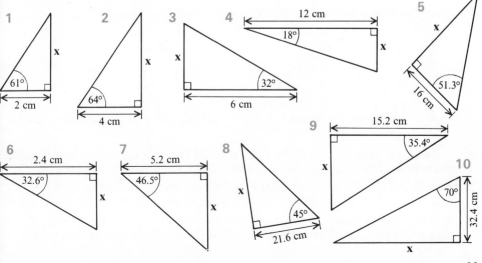

1 x 61° 2 cm

2 x 64° 4 cm

3 x

4 12 cm 18° x 32° 6 cm

5 x 16 cm 51.3°

6 2.4 cm 32.6° x

7 5.2 cm 46.5° x

8 x x 45° 21.6 cm

9 15.2 cm 35.4° x

10 70° 32.4 cm x

Tangents

Sketch diagrams to help you solve these problems. Give the answers to three significant figures.

11 If you stand 200 metres away from the bottom of a tower, the angle of elevation of its top is 25°. Find the height of the tower.

12 A boat is 600 m from a vertical cliff. The angle of elevation of the cliff-top from the boat is 11.3°. Find the height of the cliff.

13 When the altitude of the sun is 39°, a lamp-post casts a shadow 21.1 m long. Find the height of the lamp-post.

14 An isosceles triangle has two base angles of 78° each and its base is 8.4 cm long. Find   a   the height of the triangle   b   its area.

15 A ladder leans against a wall so that its inclination to the ground is 59.2°. If the foot of the ladder is 2.5 m out from the wall, how far up the wall does it reach?

16 A garage is 4.8 m wide and its roof rises at an angle of 19.3° as shown. Find the height h of the ridge above the top of the walls.

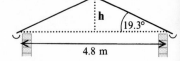

17 The angle of elevation of a mountain top from where I stand is 4.6°. If the mountain is 12.5 km away from me, how high is its top above my position?

18 Fort William in Scotland is at sea-level and 6.8 km away from Ben Nevis. The angle of elevation of the summit of Ben Nevis from Fort William is 11.2°. Find the height of Ben Nevis   a   in km   b   in metres.

19 A boy wants to find the width of a canal without crossing it. There are two posts P and Q directly opposite each other across the canal. From P, he walks 80 m along the bank to point R and measures angle PRQ as 12°. Sketch a diagram of the situation, and calculate the width of the canal.

20

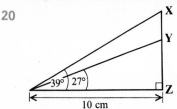

Find the lengths XZ, YZ and hence XY in this diagram.

21 Find the angle α and the length x in each of these four triangles.

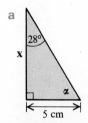 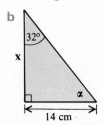 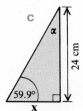 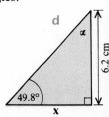

22 A cliff is 160 m high. The angle of elevation of the cliff-top from a buoy floating in the sea is 14°. Find how far the buoy is from the bottom of the cliff.

23 A circle, centre O, has a chord AB 12.4 cm long, with M as the midpoint of AB. If the angle AOB is 96°, find   a   the angle MOA b   the length MO.

24 A ladder leans against a vertical wall so that it reaches 8.5 m up the wall. If it makes an angle of 65° with the ground, how far is the foot of the ladder from the wall?

Tangents

Part 3   A mixture

Find the angle α or the length x in these triangles. Give the answers to three significant figures.

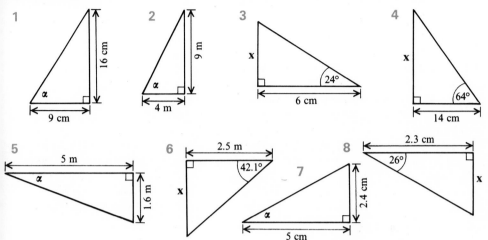

9 Find the angle θ and the length y in this diagram.

10 Find the length z and the angle ϕ in this diagram.

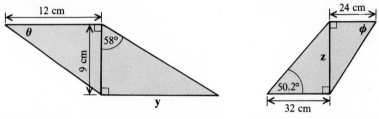

Sketch diagrams to help solve these problems. Give the answers to three significant figures.

11 A telegraph pole is held vertical by a wire from its top fixed to a point 4.5 m from the foot of the pole. If this wire makes an angle of 75° with the ground, how high is the pole?

12 A swimmer 120 m from the base of a cliff sees a coastguard on the cliff-top. If his angle of elevation from the swimmer is 23°, what is the height of the cliff?

13 A mountain rises 1.2 km above where I am standing. If it is 9 km away from me, what is the angle of elevation of its top from my position?

14 The drive to a house rises 3.5 m over a horizontal distance of 21 m. What angle does it make with the horizontal?

15 Electricity transmission lines leave a power-station P and run 25 km due north to a substation S from which they run a further 15 km due east to reach a town T. Calculate the bearing of the town from the power-station.

16

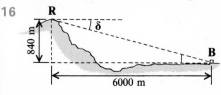

From the top of Roughfell R the village of Beckthwaite B can be seen. My map tells me that it is 6000 m away and 840 m below me. What is the angle of depression δ of Beckthwaite from the top of Roughfell?

Tangents

17 A straight road climbs a hill as it covers a horizontal distance of 3 km. If it is rising at an angle of 6°, how high is the hill in metres?

18 A fir tree casts a shadow 8.5 m long when the altitude of the sun is 64°. How tall is the tree?

19 A water pipe from a reservoir runs through a tunnel which falls vertically 350 m over a horizontal distance of 1.4 km. Find the angle which the pipe makes with the horizontal.

20 The town of Llanberis in North Wales is 6.6 km from Snowdon.
The angle of elevation of the summit of Snowdon is 8.2°. Find
a   the height of Snowdon above Llanberis, in metres
b   the height of Snowdon above sea-level if Llanberis itself is 140 m above sea-level.

21 A ship leaves Ayport on a bearing of 023° and sails 156 km to reach Bemouth. It then turns onto a bearing of 113° to sail a further 208 km to reach Cebay. Find
a   angle ABC b   angle BAC c   the bearing of Cebay from Ayport, to the nearest degree.

22 A lighthouse AC has a platform B running around its outside. A buoy X is in the sea 350 m from the lighthouse, and the angles of elevation of A and B from the buoy are 19° and 17° as shown. Find to the nearest metre
a   the height of the lighthouse AC
b   the distance AB.

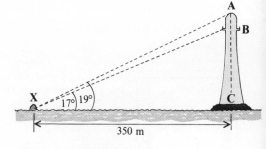

23 A coastguard C on a cliff CD 105 m high sees a swimmer S making for a buoy B. If the angles of depression of S and B from C are 12° and 19° respectively, find
a   angles DCB and DCS
b   the distance BD
c   the distance BS.

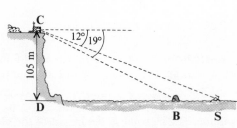

24 A rhombus has diagonals 15 cm and 9 cm long. Calculate the size of each of the four angles of the rhombus.

Cosines

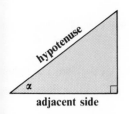

adjacent side

The cosine of angle $\alpha = \dfrac{\text{the length of the adjacent side}}{\text{the length of the hypotenuse}}$

In short, $\qquad \cos \alpha = \dfrac{\text{adjacent}}{\text{hypotenuse}}$.

Part 1   Finding an angle

Find the lettered angles in these triangles. The diagrams are *not* to scale.

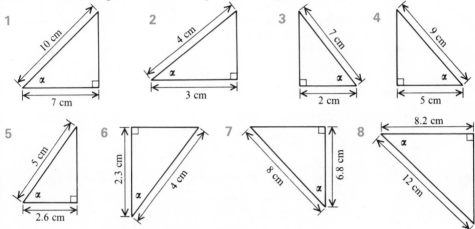

Sketch diagrams to help solve these problems.

9   A ladder is 8 m long and leans against a vertical wall so that its foot is 3 m from the wall. At what angle is it inclined to the ground?

10   A rectangle $ABCD$ has a side AB 5 cm long and a diagonal AC 9 cm long. Calculate angle BAC.

11   A telegraph pole is held vertical by a wire 12 m long which is fixed to the ground 5 m from the foot of the pole. Find the angle which the wire makes with the ground.

12   A road rises steadily for 2 km as it covers a horizontal distance of 1.9 km. What angle does the road make with the horizontal?

13   A circle of radius OA 7 cm long has a chord AB 10 cm long with a midpoint M. Calculate the size of angle OAM.

14   I leave point A and walk 5 km due north to reach point B, where I turn due east and continue until I reach point C. If the shortest distance between A and C is 8 km, on what bearing is C from A to the nearest degree?

Division by a decimal

Find the lettered angles in these triangles.

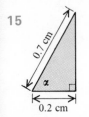

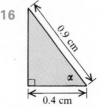

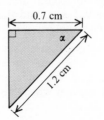

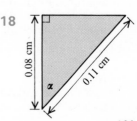

Cosines

19 A pipe of length 0.6 km is laid on sloping ground to carry water across a horizontal distance of 0.56 km. Find the angle which the pipe makes with the horizontal.

20 A line of pylons carries electricity cables for a distance of 0.25 km down the side of the hill. In this distance they cover 0.21 km horizontally. Find the angle which the hillside makes with the horizontal.

21 The gable end of a garden shed covers a span of 1.8 metres.
If the slanting roof is 1.1 metres long, at what angle α does it slant?

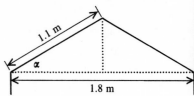

22 An isosceles triangle has $AB = AC = 1.5$ cm and $BC = 0.8$ cm. If the midpoint of BC is M, calculate angle ABM.

Division by cancelling

Find the lettered angles in these triangles.

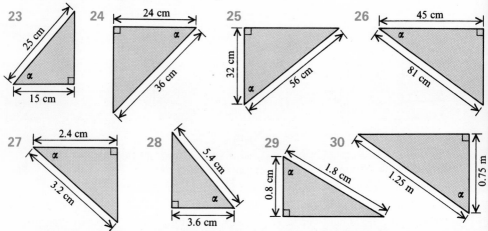

31 A ladder 12 m long leans against a house so that its lower end is 3 m from the bottom of the house wall. Find the angle between the ladder and the ground.

32 A skier travels 350 m down a snow-covered slope and covers a horizontal distance of 280 m. Find the inclination of the slope to the horizontal.

33 A man leaves point A and walks 2.7 km due north. He then turns and walks due east until he reaches point B. If $AB = 4.5$ km, find the bearing of B from A, to the nearest degree.

34 The diagonal of a rectangle is 5.4 cm long. If one of the sides of the rectangle is 3.6 cm long, find the angle between this side and the diagonal.

35 A barrel rolls 2.1 m down a plank from the back of a lorry. If the horizontal distance covered by the barrel is 1.8 m, find the angle made by the plank with the ground.

36 A young girl on a swing is 3 m higher in her topmost position than when she started. If the ropes are 7.2 m long, find the angle θ that the ropes make with the vertical when she is at her highest.

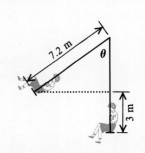

Cosines

Division by logarithms or calculator

Find the lettered angles in these triangles.

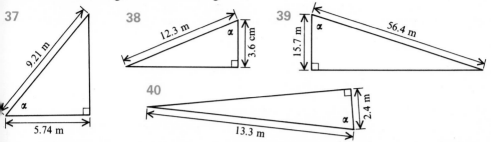

41 A radio aerial is held upright by a wire 124 m long which is fixed to the top of the aerial and to the ground at a point 49 m from the foot of the aerial. What is the inclination of the wire to the ground?

42 Driffield is 11.2 miles due north of Beverley and Lissett is due east of Driffield. If it is 13.6 km from Lissett to Beverley, calculate the bearing of Lissett from Beverley to the nearest degree.

43 A circle centre O has a radius OA 7.6 cm long. A tangent AB is drawn at A and the distance OB is 18.7 cm. Calculate the angle AOB.

44 An aeroplane takes off and travels a distance of 24.6 km as it climbs. Its shadow covers a distance of 21.5 km on level ground. At what angle is the aeroplane climbing?

45 An isosceles triangle has $PQ = PR = 20.6$ cm and $QR = 9.6$ cm. Calculate the three angles of the triangle.

46 The tops of two vertical poles of different heights are joined by a straight telephone wire 47 metres long. If the poles are 37.5 metres apart, find the inclination of the wire to the horizontal.

Part 2   Finding a side

Find the lettered lengths in these triangles, giving the answers to three significant figures. The triangles are *not* drawn to scale.

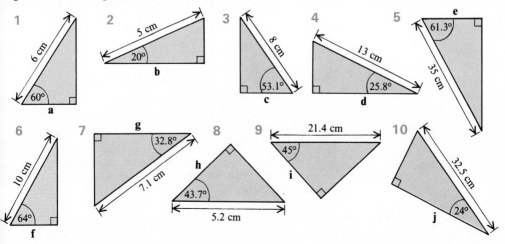

Cosines

Sketch diagrams to help solve these problems.

11 A lorry is driven 4.2 km along a motorway which is gradually climbing at an angle of 18°. What horizontal distance has it travelled?

12 An aircraft takes off and climbs for 2.5 km at an angle of 23°. What distance does its shadow travel on the level ground?

13 Ornsay is 10.5 km from Armadale on a bearing of 031°. How much further north is Ornsay than Armadale?

14 A ladder is extended to a length of 10.4 m to lean against a wall at an angle of 75° to the ground. How far from the foot of the wall is the bottom of the ladder?

15 My friend John is flying a kite at the end of a 46-m length of string which makes an angle of 27° with the ground. If I leave John to go and stand directly beneath the kite, how far do I walk?

16 A flag-pole is held in a vertical position by a wire 8.5 m long sloping at an angle of 55° to the ground. How far from the foot of the pole is the wire fixed to the ground?

17 An isosceles triangle FGH has $FG = FH = 12.6$ cm. If angle FGH is 72° and M is the midpoint of GH, calculate the length of
   a GM b GH.

18 A roof with a slant length of 7.4 metres slopes at an angle of 40° as shown. Calculate the span s which the roof is covering.

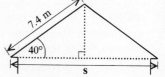

19 The equal legs of a step-ladder are 1.8 metres long and inclined at $62\frac{1}{2}°$ to the horizontal when the ladder is standing upright. Find the distance between the feet of the ladder.

20 A ship leaves port P and sails on a bearing of 015° to reach harbour H. It then sails on a bearing of 105° from the harbour to reach the dock D. The shortest distance from P to D is 145 km, and the bearing of D from P is 050°. Find
   a angle PHD b angle HPD c the distance from P to H.

21 Find the lengths x and y in this diagram.

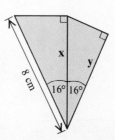

22

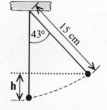

A metal bob swings at the end of a piece of string 15 cm long. It swings through an angle of 43° from the vertical as shown. Find the vertical height h that it rises.

Cosines

23

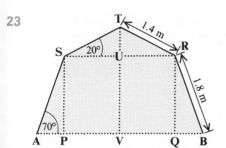

The symmetrical cross-section of a metal-framed tent is shown here. Find the distance AB across the floor of the tent.

24 The point $P(x, 6)$ is 12 units from the origin O. If OP makes an angle of 30° with the x-axis, find the x-value of the point P.

Part 3   A mixture

Find the angle α or the length x in these triangles. Give the answers to three significant figures.

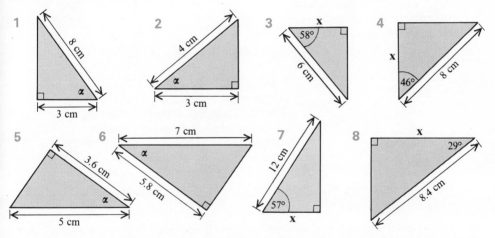

9 A plank of wood 9 m long rests against a wall so that its lower end is 4 m from the foot of the wall. What angle does the plank make with the ground?

10 The track of a funicular railway is 3.4 km long as it rises at an angle of 54° up a mountain side. What horizontal distance does it cover?

11 A boat is moored to a pier by a rope 12.6 m long. When the rope is tight it makes an angle of 35° with the pier wall. Calculate the height of the pier above the level of the boat.

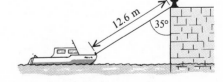

12 An aircraft takes off and after flying for 15 km it has covered 13.8 km horizontally. At what angle is it climbing?

13 A radio mast 80 m tall is held vertical by a wire 120 m long. What is the angle between the mast and the wire?

14 A ski-lift 350 m long is built on a hillside sloping at an angle of 63°. What distance does the lift cover horizontally?

Cosines

15 Calculate the lengths x and y in this diagram.

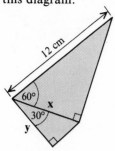

16 From the two triangles ACD and BCD, calculate the lengths AC, BC and AB.

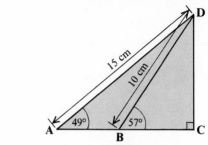

17 A vertical television mast PQ is held by four cables anchored to the ground at R, S, T and U in a straight line. If the cables are 35 m and 40 m long at angles of 50° and 42° to the ground respectively, calculate the distances QT, QU and TU.

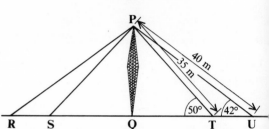

18

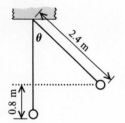

A pendulum is 2.4 m long and it swings so that its bob rises a maximum distance of 0.8 m. Calculate the maximum angle θ which the pendulum makes with the vertical.

19 The point $P(5, 12)$ is 13 units from the origin O. What angle does the line OP make with the x-axis?

20 I look down a long corridor at the door at the far end. It is open enough for me to see through half the doorway. If the door is 84 cm across, at what angle is it standing open?

Sines

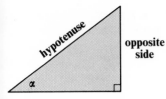

The sine of angle $\alpha = \dfrac{\text{the length of the opposite side}}{\text{the length of the hypotenuse}}$.

In short, $\qquad \sin \alpha = \dfrac{\text{opposite}}{\text{hypotenuse}}$.

Part 1   Finding an angle

Find the lettered angles in these triangles. The diagrams are *not* drawn to scale.

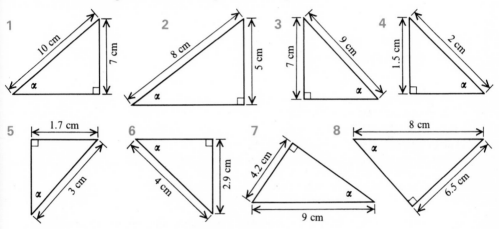

Sketch diagrams to help solve these problems.

9   A vertical flag-pole 8 m high is held by a wire 9 m long attached to its top. What angle does the wire make with the level ground?

10   A cable-car travels a distance of 7 km to climb a mountain 2 km high. Find the angle which the cable makes with the horizontal.

11   After take-off, an aeroplane flies 12 km to climb to a height of 5 km. Calculate the angle at which it is climbing.

12   In the rectangle *ABCD*, the diagonal *BD* is 8 cm long and the side *BC* is 3.5 cm long. Sketch the rectangle and calculate the size of angle *BDC*.

13   A road winds steadily uphill for 9 km before reaching a height of 1.4 km. What angle does the road make with the horizontal?

14   In an isosceles triangle *XYZ*, *XY* = *XZ* = 5 cm and the distance from *X* to the midpoint of *YZ* is 3.6 cm. Calculate the size of angle *XYZ*.

Division by a decimal

Find the lettered angles in these triangles.

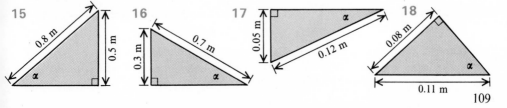

Sines

19 A small ramp with a sloping length of 0.9 metres will lift the back wheels of a car to a height of 0.4 metres. What angle does the slope of the ramp make with the horizontal?

20 A hill rises 0.3 km above the surrounding plain. What angle does a fence make with the horizontal, if it climbs the hill over a distance of 0.8 km?

21 A drain is laid across 0.15 km of sloping ground so that one end is 0.02 km higher than the other. What angle does the drain make with the horizontal?

22 An isosceles triangle PQR has $PQ = PR = 0.12$ m. If M is the midpoint of QR and $PM = 0.07$ m, calculate the size of angle PQR.

Division by cancelling

Find the lettered angles in these triangles.

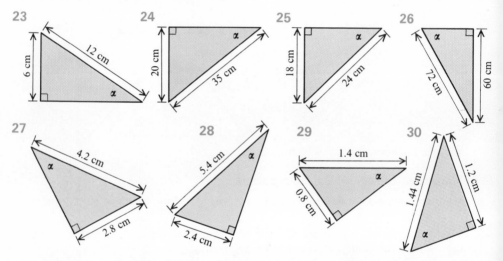

23 24 25 26

27 28 29 30

31 A kite is flying 18 m high at the end of 72 m of string. If the string is straight, find the angle it makes with the ground.

32 A telegraph pole 7.2 m high is held vertical by a sloping wire 9.0 m long fixed to its top and anchored in the ground. Find the angle which the wire makes with the ground.

33 A cyclist pushes his bike uphill along a road for 162 m. If at the top he has ascended 36 m, find the inclination of the road to the horizontal.

34 A circle, centre O and radius 25 cm, has a chord AB 20 cm long with a midpoint M. Find
a   angle AOM b   angle AOB.

35 A ladder 8 m long reaches 5.5 m up a vertical wall. What angle does it make with the ground?

36 Askham is due north of Bugthorpe. If you walk 6.4 km due east from Askham you reach Cudworth. It is 7.2 km direct from Bugthorpe to Cudworth. What is the bearing of Cudworth from Bugthorpe to the nearest degree?

Sines

Division by logarithms or a calculator

Find the lettered angles in these triangles.

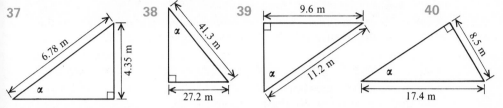

37 6.78 m, 4.35 m, α

38 α, 41.3 m, 27.2 m

39 9.6 m, 11.2 m, α

40 8.5 m, 17.4 m, α

41 A rectangle $WXYZ$ has diagonals 5.9 cm long. If $XY = 4.1$ cm, find the size of angle XWY.

42 A rhombus has sides 3.8 cm long and one diagonal 7.0 cm long. Calculate
 a the angle between the other diagonal and any side
 b all four angles of the rhombus.

43 A gamekeeper walks 437 m up the side of a hill and finds that he has risen vertically by 249 m. Find the inclination of the hill to the horizontal.

44 On take-off, an aircraft has to fly 58.5 km to rise to its cruising height of 3250 metres. At what angle does it have to climb?

45 The roof of a shed slants 4.45 m from its ridge to its gutter and the vertical rise is 1.45 m. Find the angle of inclination of the roof to the horizontal.

46 Laikby is 5.4 km due east of Playford. Caperham is due south of Playford. Find the bearing of Laikby from Caperham (to the nearest degree), if the shortest distance between them is 8.7 km.

Part 2 Finding a side

Find the lettered lengths in these triangles, giving the answers to three significant figures. The triangles are *not* drawn to scale.

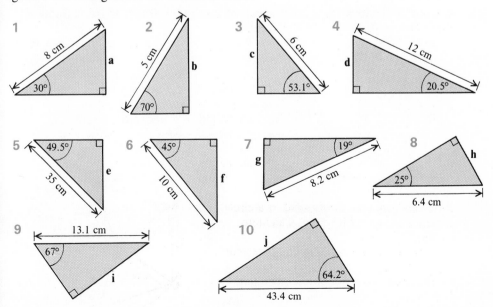

1 8 cm, 30°, a

2 5 cm, 70°, b

3 c, 6 cm, 53.1°

4 12 cm, 20.5°, d

5 49.5°, 35 cm, e

6 45°, 10 cm, f

7 g, 19°, 8.2 cm

8 25°, 6.4 cm, h

9 13.1 cm, 67°, i

10 j, 64.2°, 43.4 cm

Sines

Sketch diagrams to help solve these problems. Give the answers to three significant figures.

11 A kite flies in a strong wind with the string at an angle of 21° to the ground. Find the height of the kite, if 84 metres of string is let out.

12 In a children's playground, a slide 10.5 metres long is inclined at 25° to the ground. If one end is on the ground, at what height is the other end?

13 A model aircraft flying in a circle is guided by a control-line 24 m long making an angle of 38° with the ground. Find the height of the aircraft above ground level.

14 A mountain railway climbs up a track inclined at 7° to the horizontal. What height will the train rise as it travels along 2.5 km of track   a in km   b in metres?

15 A straight road runs due north. I leave the road and walk on a bearing of 035° for 3.2 km. What is the shortest distance I would then have to walk to get back to the road?

16 In an isosceles triangle, $AB = AC = 24$ cm and M is the midpoint of BC. If angle $BAC = 144°$, calculate the lengths of BM and BC.

17 A pair of compasses is opened so that the angle between the two arms is 64°. If the arms are 8.4 cm long, what is the distance between the two points?

18 A cone standing on a table has a slant length of 12.3 cm at an angle of 61° to the table. What is the height of the cone?

19 A tripod has legs 1.2 metres long slanting at an angle of 68° to the floor. Calculate the height of the top of the tripod above the floor.

20 Find the lengths x and y in this diagram.

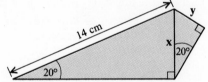

21 A circle, centre O, has a point T on its circumference. A point P, outside the circle, is 21 cm from O and PT is a tangent to the circle. If angle $TPO = 32°$, find the radius of the circle.

22 A chord PQ is drawn in a circle, centre O and radius 4 cm. M is the midpoint of PQ and angle $POQ = 150°$. Calculate
a   angle POM b   the length PM c   the length of the chord PQ.

23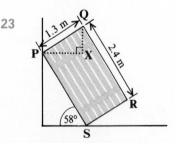

A crate with a rectangular cross-section $PQRS$ 2.4 m by 1.3 m leans against a wall at an angle of 58° as shown. Find
a   the height of P above the floor
b   the size of $\angle SPX$ and $\angle QPX$
c   the height of Q above P
d   the height of Q above the floor.

24 A regular pentagon is inscribed in a circle of centre O and radius 5 cm. Calculate
a   angle α
b   angle MOB, where M is the midpoint of side AB
c   the length of a side of the pentagon.

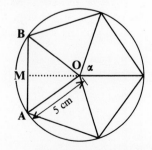

Sines

Part 3   A mixture

Find the angle α or the length x in these triangles. Give the answers to three significant figures.

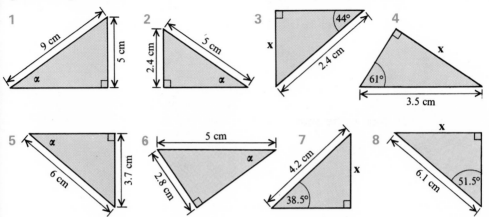

9   Boxes are slid down a chute 20 metres long from the upper floor of a warehouse 9.5 metres high. What is the inclination of the chute to the horizontal?

10   In triangle OPQ, $OP = OQ = 2.5$ cm and $PQ = 4$ cm. If M is the midpoint of PQ, calculate $\angle POM$ and $\angle POQ$.

11   The two sides of a step ladder are 1.5 m long and when fully open the angle between them is 32°. Calculate the distance between their feet when in this position.

12   An equilateral triangle has sides 15 cm long. State the size of the angles of any equilateral triangle and calculate the distance from one corner of this triangle to the midpoint of the opposite side.

13   The line AB is a tangent to a circle at A and B is 9 cm from the centre O of the circle. If the radius of the circle is 5.5 cm, calculate angle ABO.

14   A circle has a diameter YZ of 12 cm. A point X lies on the circumference of the circle at a distance of 3.8 cm from Y. Calculate angle XZY.

15   The point P has a y-coordinate of 2 units. The line joining P to the origin O has a length of 5 units. Calculate the angle which OP makes with the x-axis.

16   The point $Q(9, y)$ is joined to the origin O so that the line OQ makes an angle of 53.1° with the x-axis. If the length of OQ is 15 units, find the y-coordinate of Q.

17   An isosceles trapezium $PQRS$ has parallel sides PQ and SR and equal sides PS and QR. If PS is 8.5 cm long and makes an angle of 54° with SR, calculate the height h of the trapezium.

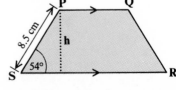

18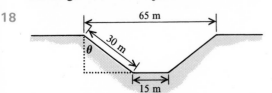

A railway cutting is 15 metres wide at the bottom and 65 metres wide at the top. Both sloping sides are 30 metres long. Calculate the angle θ which the sides make with the vertical.

Sines

19 A pyramid has a square base with diagonals 12.8 cm long. If its slanting edges are 9 cm long, calculate the angle θ which the slanting edges make with the vertical.

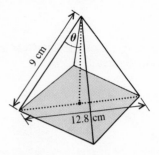

20

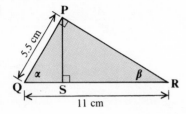

a Use triangle PQR to calculate angle β.
b Write without further calculation the size of angle α.
c Calculate the length PS.

Sines, cosines and tangents

A mnemonic

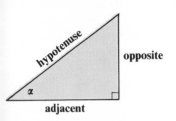

$$\sin \alpha = \frac{\text{opposite}}{\text{hypotenuse}}$$ S O H   Some Old Harvesters

$$\cos \alpha = \frac{\text{adjacent}}{\text{hypotenuse}}$$ C A H   Can Always Have

$$\tan \alpha = \frac{\text{opposite}}{\text{adjacent}}$$ T O A   Tankards Of Ale

Part 1   Finding an angle

Calculate the lettered angles in these triangles.

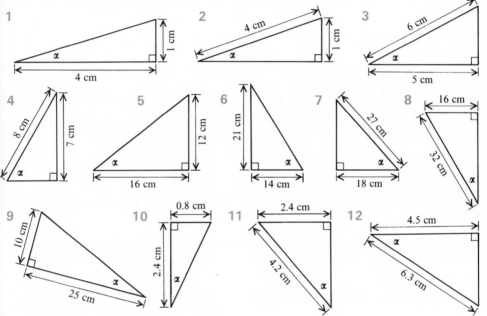

Sketch diagrams to help solve these problems.

13 A ladder 15 metres long leans against a vertical wall so that the top of the ladder is 12 metres above the ground. What angle does the ladder make
   a   with the ground   b   with the wall?

14 An aeroplane takes off and after travelling 3500 metres it has risen 420 metres above ground level. At what angle is it climbing?

15 A tunnel to a mountain reservoir is 4500 metres long and one end is 180 metres higher than the other. At what angle is the tunnel rising?

16 A straight road climbs a hill 600 m high. If the road is 1500 m long, find the angle at which it is climbing.

17 Triangle ABC is isosceles with $AB = AC = 16$ cm and $BC = 12$ cm. Sketch the triangle and draw the line AM where M is the midpoint of BC. Calculate angle ABC.

Sines, cosines and tangents

18 The two arms *XY* and *XZ* of a pair of dividers are 18 cm long. They are opened so that their points *Y* and *Z* are 8 cm apart. Calculate angle *XYZ*.

19 The pole of a bell-tent is 2 m high and the diameter of the base of the tent is 5 m. What angle does the slant side of the tent make with the ground?

20 The sides of a rectangle are 8 cm and 10 cm long. What are the angles between its diagonals?

21 A picture is hung from a nail *N* by a string 60 cm long fixed to two points *A* and *B* 40 cm apart. Calculate angle *NAB*.

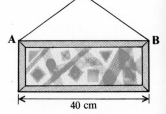

22 *ABCD* is a square with *M* the midpoint of side *AB*. If the sides are 20 cm long, find
  a angle *AMD*   b angle *ADM*.

23 A boat is anchored to the sea-bed by a straight chain 14.4 m long. If the sea is 8.4 m deep, what angle does the chain make with the sea-bed?

24 A rectangle is 6.4 cm long and 2.4 cm wide. Find the angle between a diagonal and a long side.

25 I walk 3.6 km from point *A* to reach point *B*. If *B* is 2.7 km further east than *A*, find the bearing on which I walked, to the nearest degree.

26 A sloping roof is 5.6 m long and the top of the roof is 3.5 m higher than its bottom. Find the angle which the roof makes with the horizontal.

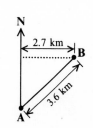

Part 2   Finding a side

Find the lettered lengths in these triangles. Give the answers to three significant figures.

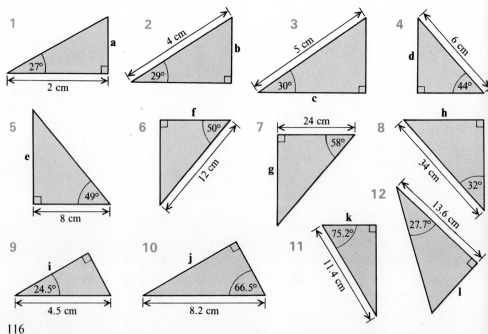

Sines, cosines and tangents

13 A ladder 8 metres long leans against a vertical wall so that its angle with the ground is 61°. Find how far up the wall the ladder reaches.

14 A kite is flying at the end of 42 metres of string. If the string rises at an angle of 49°, how far above the ground is the kite?

15 A square has a diagonal 25 cm long.
   a What is the size of the angle between the diagonal and a side of the square?
   b Calculate the length of a side of the square.

16 A rectangle has a diagonal 14 cm long and the angle between the diagonal and a long side is 29°. Calculate the length of
   a a long side   b a short side.

17 I leave point Y and walk on a bearing of 035° for 1.5 km to reach point Z. How far is
   a Z to the north of Y   b Z to the east of Y?

18 A man leaves point L and walks 3.4 km due north to arrive at point M. He then leaves M and walks due east to reach point N. If the bearing of N from L is 080°, find the distance MN.

19 An isosceles triangle PQR has PQ = PR = 2.6 cm and the base angles Q and R are 60.5°. Join P to the midpoint of QR and calculate the length QR.

20 The legs of a pair of dividers are 9.5 cm long and opened at an angle of 29°. Calculate the distance between the ends of the two legs.

21 This diagram represents the roof of a small bungalow. Find the height h of the central ridge R above the tops of the walls A and C.

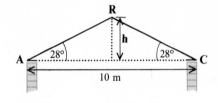

22 The chord of a circle subtends an angle of 140° at the centre of the circle. If the radius of the circle is 15 cm, find the length of the chord.

23

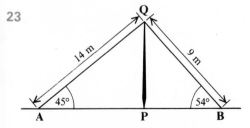

A mast PQ is held vertical by two wires anchored to the ground at points A and B so that A, P and B are in a straight line. If the wires are 14 m and 9 m long slanting at the angles shown, calculate the distance between A and B.

24 A man sitting at a window can just see the sun over a rooftop 10 m away from him horizontally. If the altitude of the sun is 36½° and his eye is 7 m above ground level, find the height h of the roof above the ground.

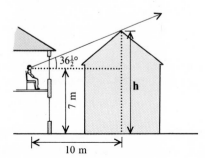

Sines, cosines and tangents

25 This diagram shows a section of a railway cutting with a level bottom BC 5 m wide. The tops of the embankments A and D are both 6 m above BC. Calculate the distance between A and D.

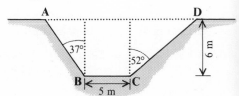

26

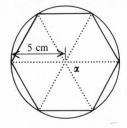

A regular hexagon is inscribed in a circle of radius 5 cm.

a What angle α does each side subtend at the centre of the circle?

b Calculate the length of a side.

Part 3 Finding a hypotenuse

Find the length of the hypotenuse in these triangles.

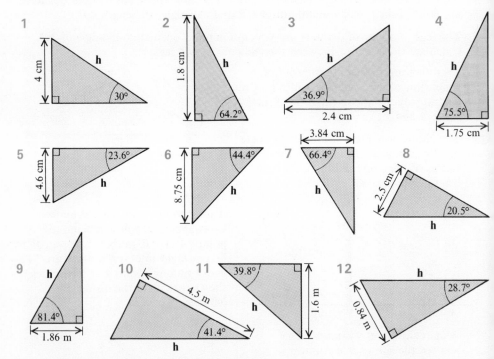

13 Use long division, logarithms, reciprocal tables or a calculator to find the length h of the hypotenuse in this triangle when

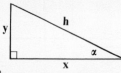

a $\alpha = 48°$, $x = 8.7$ cm   b $\alpha = 52°$, $x = 6.4$ cm

c $\alpha = 67°$, $y = 9.25$ cm   d $\alpha = 72\frac{1}{2}°$, $x = 14.3$ cm

e $\alpha = 30\frac{1}{2}°$, $y = 18.7$ cm   f $\alpha = 24.6°$, $y = 20.8$ cm

g $\alpha = 76.2°$, $x = 7.75$ cm   h $\alpha = 45.8°$, $y = 11.7$ cm.

Sines, cosines and tangents

14 When a kite flies at a height of 20.5 m, the string makes an angle of 30° with the ground. What is the length of the string?

15 If a railway line climbs 120 m vertically on track inclined at 8.6° to the horizontal, what is the length of the track?

16 The diagonal *PR* of the rectangle *PQRS* makes an angle of 66.4° with the side *PQ*. If *PQ* is 12 cm long, calculate the length of the diagonal *PR*.

17 A square has sides 8 cm long.
   a Write, without calculation, the size of the angle between a diagonal and a side.
   b Calculate the length of a diagonal.

18 Calculate lengths *p* and *q* in this diagram.

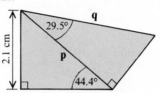

19

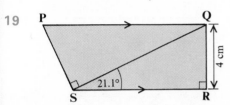

Trapezium *PQRS* has *PQ* parallel to *SR*, angle *QSR* = 21.1° and *QR* = 4 cm. Calculate
   a the length *SQ*   b angle *PQS*
   c the length *PQ*.

20 Triangle *ABC* is isosceles with *AB* = *AC* = 14 cm and *BC* = 10 cm. *O* is the centre of its circumcircle, and *M* and *N* are the midpoints of sides *BC* and *AC* respectively. Calculate

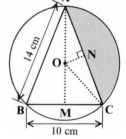

   a angle *MAC*   b angle *AON*
   c angle *AOC*   d the length *OA*
   e the length *ON*   f the area of △*AOC*
   g the area of the   h the area of sector
      circle   *AOC*
   i the area of the
      shaded segment.

Pythagoras' theorem

Part 1 Illustrating the theorem

1 A floor is covered with small tiles. Each tile is an isosceles right-angled triangle.

Six diagrams are drawn on the floor. Each diagram has a black triangle with squares drawn on each of its sides.

For each of the six diagrams below, count the number of tiles inside the three squares.

Copy this table and enter the results.

Diagram	The number of tiles inside		
	one small square X	the other small square Y	the large square Z
A	2	2	
B			
C			
D			
E			
F			

What connection is there between the results in columns X and Y and Z?

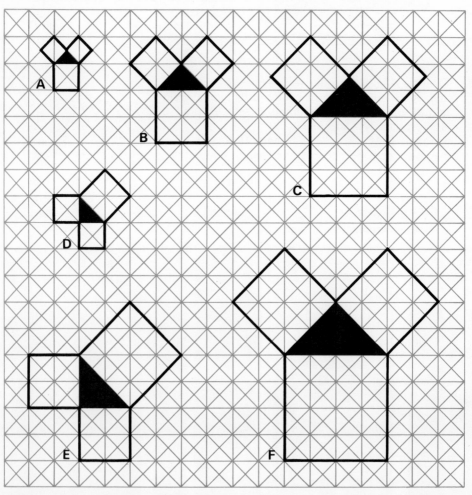

Pythagoras' theorem

2 a Using a ruler, draw the triangle *ABC* accurately onto a sheet of paper.

Use a protractor (or set square) to draw the three squares *X*, *Y* and *Z*.

Also draw the two squares *X* and *Y* separately with sides 4 cm and 8 cm long and cut these out.

Cut the larger square *Y* into four pieces along the dotted lines shown.

Can you arrange square *X* and the four pieces of *Y* to fit exactly onto square *Z*?

b Repeat the whole experiment for triangle *ABC* which has sides 3 cm and 6 cm as shown.

3 a Copy this diagram of the triangle *ABC* with squares *X* and *Y*. (Or trace it —it is drawn here full size.)

Cut round the outside of the diagram.

Find the centre of square *Y* and label the point *O*.

Draw a line through *O* parallel to *AC*.

Draw a line through *O* perpendicular to *AC*.

Cut off squares *X* and *Y* from triangle *ABC*.

Cut *Y* into 4 pieces along the dotted lines.

Can your arrange square *X* with the four pieces of *Y* to make one larger square on the side *AC* of the triangle?

b Choose any other sized right-angled triangle. Repeat these instructions to make one large square on side *AC* from the squares *X* and *Y*.

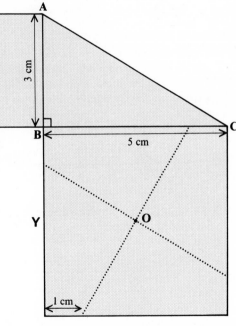

Pythagoras' theorem

4

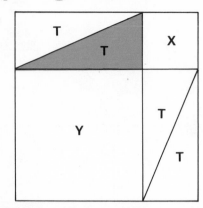 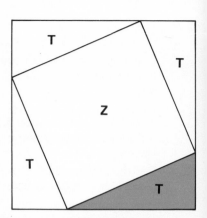

These two large squares are the same size but they have been cut up in two different ways.

X, Y and Z are the three squares on the sides of the shaded triangle T.

The area of the left hand square $= 4T + X + Y$.

The area of the right hand square $= 4T + Z$.

What relationship is there between the areas of the squares X, Y and Z?

5 **By accurate drawing**

Draw each of the right-angled triangles whose sides a and b are given in cm in the six rows of the table. Use a ruler and protractor (or set square) and be as accurate as possible.

Measure the length of the hypotenuse c of each triangle with a ruler.

Copy this table and enter the values of a, b and c. Complete each row, using square tables if necessary.

There is no need to draw the three squares X, Y and Z to work out the areas. The lengths are in cm, so the areas are in cm².

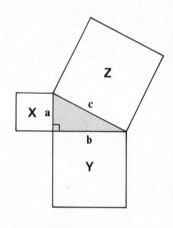

	a	b	c	Area of X a^2	Area of Y b^2	Area of Z c^2	$a^2 + b^2$
1st triangle	3	4		9	16		
2nd triangle	2	3					
3rd triangle	4	5					
4th triangle	2	5					
5th triangle	3.5	4					
6th triangle	2.5	5.5					

What do you notice about the results in the last two columns of the table?

Pythagoras' theorem

6 Testing to see if a triangle is right-angled

So far in this chapter the exercises have illustrated Pythagoras' Theorem, which states that

> In any right-angled triangle, the square on the hypotenuse is equal in area to the sum of the squares on the other two sides.

We can now use this theorem to test if a triangle is right-angled.

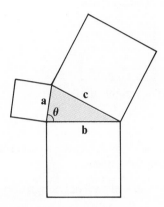

Each of the twelve triangles in the table has sides of length a, b and c in centimetres as shown.

Copy the table and complete each row using the values of a, b and c as given.

Answer the final question YES or NO.

	Sides			Area of squares				Is angle θ a right angle?
	a	b	c	a^2	b^2	c^2	$a^2 + b^2$	
a	3	4	5					
b	4	5	6					
c	2	3	4					
d	6	8	10					
e	5	6	7					
f	5	9	10					
g	5	12	13					
h	4	8	10					
i	9	12	15					
j	7	24	25					
k	8	15	17					
l	14	48	50					

Pythagoras' theorem

7

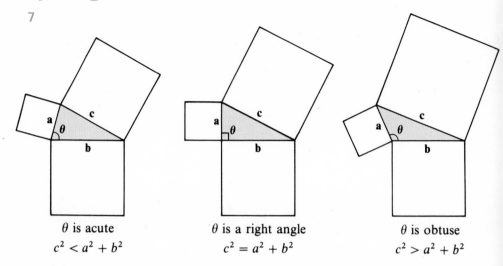

θ is acute	θ is a right angle	θ is obtuse
$c^2 < a^2 + b^2$	$c^2 = a^2 + b^2$	$c^2 > a^2 + b^2$

Comparing the value of c^2 with $a^2 + b^2$ indicates whether a triangle is acute-angled, right-angled or obtuse-angled.

Copy this table which gives the sides of twelve triangles, in centimetres.

Complete each row and answer the final question by entering one word **acute**, **right** or **obtuse**.

	Sides			Areas of squares				What type of
	a	b	c	a^2	b^2	c^2	$a^2 + b^2$	angle is θ?
a	2	3	4					
b	3	4	5					
c	1	2	3					
d	3	5	6					
e	3	3	4					
f	6	8	10					
g	5	7	8					
h	6	9	12					
i	7	8	9					
j	10	15	21					
k	9	40	41					
l	11	22	24					

Pythagoras' theorem

Part 2   Using square- and square-root tables

Calculate the lettered lengths in these right-angled triangles.

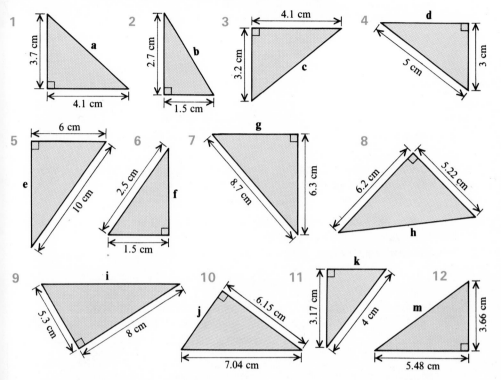

Draw diagrams for these problems and give the answers to three significant figures.

13 A plank of wood leans against a wall with its upper end 4.6 m off the ground and its lower end 3.2 m from the foot of the wall. How long is the plank?

14 A skier travels down a steep hill losing a vertical height of 1.08 km as he covers 2.14 km horizontally. Calculate the actual distance he skis down the hillside.

15 A flight of stairs in a large building takes up a horizontal distance of 7.6 metres. If I have to walk 9.2 metres to climb the stairs, what vertical distance have I risen?

16 A telegraph pole 7.5 m high is held firm by a wire fixed to its top and to a point in the ground 6.2 m from the foot of the pole. How long is the wire?

17 Calculate the length of a diagonal of
    a   a rectangle 5.75 m by 6.05 m   b   a square of side 4.96 m.

18 Calculate the height AM of an isosceles triangle ABC in which $AB = AC = 8.7$ cm, $BC = 10.4$ cm and M is the midpoint of BC.

19 Calculate the height of an equilateral triangle with sides 10 cm long.

20 A circle, centre O, contains a chord AB 14 cm long. If the midpoint M of AB is 4.5 cm from O, calculate the radius of the circle.

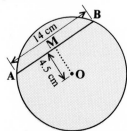

Pythagoras' theorem

21 A circle with centre C and radius 9.4 cm contains a chord PQ such that its midpoint M is 5.7 cm from C. Calculate the length of the chord PQ.

22 A cone has a base diameter of 16.5 cm and a vertical height of 4.8 cm. Calculate the slant height of the cone.

23 A ship leaves port and sails 7.3 km due east then 5.8 km due south to reach harbour. What is the shortest distance between the port and the harbour?

24 A railway track climbs a hill 1.25 km high as it covers a horizontal distance of 9.75 km. What is the length of the track?

25 A map shows a line of pylons to be 8.24 km long, but they are in fact climbing a hill 1.04 km high. Calculate the true length of the line.

26 A rectangle has a diagonal of 4.2 cm and its shorter sides are 2.3 cm long. What is the length of its longer sides?

27 A ladder 5.7 m long rests against a wall so that its foot is 1.8 m from the foot of the wall. How high up the wall does the ladder reach?

28 Calculate the height of an equilateral triangle of side 9 cm.

29 A rhombus has sides of 6.25 metres. If one of its diagonals is 5.68 metres long, find the length of its other diagonal.

30 M is the midpoint of side AB of rectangle $ABCD$. If $AB = 6.8$ cm and $AD = 3.1$ cm, calculate the length MD.

31 Find the lengths a and b, and hence find the area of triangle PQR.

32 Find the lengths x and y and hence find the area of triangle ABD.

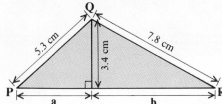

Part 3 Involving numbers greater than 100

Calculate the length of the hypotenuse in these right-angled triangles.

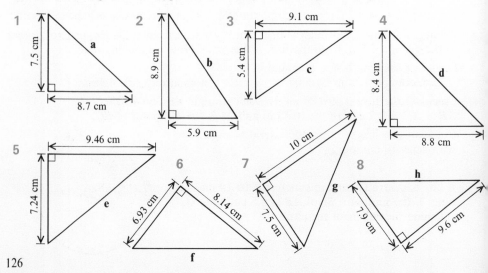

Pythagoras' theorem

.ketch a diagram to help solve these problems and give the answers to three
ignificant figures.

9 A man walks 8.7 km due north and then turns to walk a further 6.2 km due
east. What is the shortest distance he now has to walk to return to his starting
point?

0 A chimney 7.5 metres high casts a shadow 8.6 metres long on level ground.
How far is it from the top of the chimney to the end of its shadow?

1 A rectangle has sides of 6.8 cm and 9.3 cm. Find the length of its diagonals.

2 Calculate the length of the diagonals of a square of side 8.75 cm.

3 A rectangular playground is 9.8 metres by 8.4 metres. What is the furthest
distance a young child can run in a straight line in this playground?

4 A circle with centre O and radius 6.25 cm has a tangent AB which touches the
circle at A. If $AB = 9.75$ cm, calculate the length OB.

5 How far from the origin is the point $(8\frac{1}{2}, 9)$?

'alculate the lettered lengths in these right-angled triangles, giving the answers to
hree significant figures.

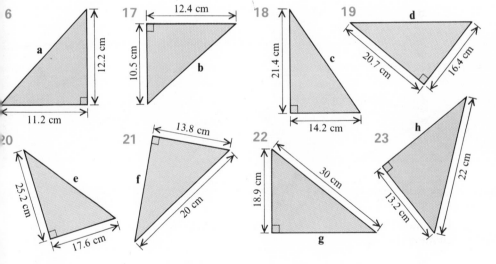

24 Calculate the length of the third side of this right-angled triangle, when the
lengths of the other two sides are given. Find

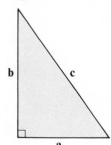

     a c when $a = 14.3$ cm, $b = 30.3$ cm

     b c when $a = 20$ cm, $b = 42.1$ cm

     c b when $a = 30$ cm, $c = 50$ cm

     d b when $a = 25.7$ cm, $c = 48.7$ cm

     e b when $a = 31.7$ cm, $c = 52.3$ cm

     f c when $a = 47.8$ cm, $b = 51.3$ cm

     g a when $b = 60.7$ cm, $c = 72.3$ cm

     h c when $a = 57.4$ cm, $b = 64.1$ cm.

25 A ship leaves port A and sails 27.5 km due south to reach port B. From port B
it sails 42.5 km due west to arrive at port C. How far is C directly from A?

127

Pythagoras' theorem

26 An isosceles triangle has two sides 18.4 cm long and the third side is 14.6 cm long. Find   a   the height of the triangle   b   its area.

27 A cone 21 cm high has a base of radius 12.5 cm. Calculate its slant length.

28 A square has a diagonal of length 25 cm. Find the length of one of its sides.

29 A chord of a circle is 36 cm long. The radius of the circle is 20.5 cm. Find how far the midpoint of the chord is from the centre of the circle.

30 A circle, centre *O*, has a radius *OT* 9.5 cm long. A point *P* lies on the tangent which touches the circle at *T*, so that *PT* = 14.2 cm. Find the distance *OP*.

Part 4   Further problems

Unless otherwise stated, give answers to three significant figures.

1 Calculate the lengths *x* and *y* in these diagrams, where all lengths are given in centimetres.

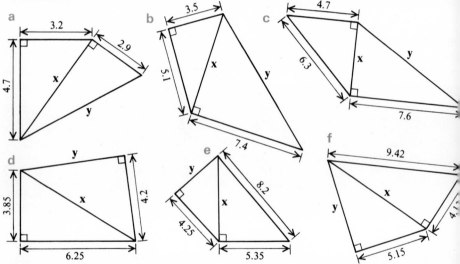

2 Calculate the lengths *x* and *y* in these diagrams, where all lengths are given in centimetres.

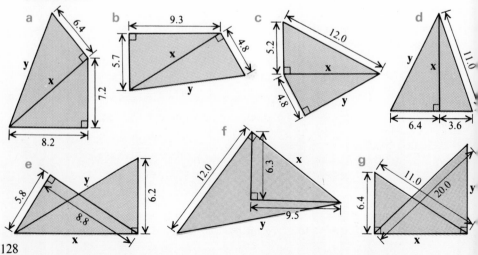

Pythagoras' theorem

3 Calculate the lengths *m* and *n*.

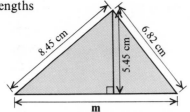 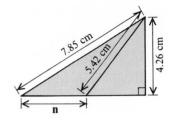

4 Calculate the lengths *BD* and *AD*.

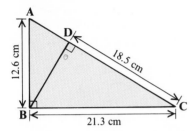

5 Calculate the lengths *QR* and *PS*.

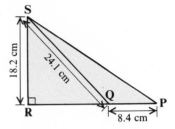

6 Prove that each of the triangles *ABC* is right-angled at *B*.

a

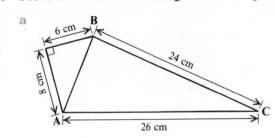

b

c

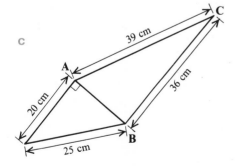

d

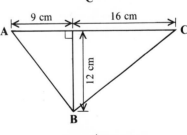

7 A square of side 4 cm contains triangle *ABC*. Use each of the three shaded triangles to calculate the sides of triangle *ABC* and hence prove that triangle *ABC* is right-angled at *B*.

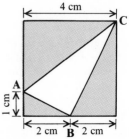

Pythagoras' theorem

8 The centres of four identical touching coins of radius 1.5 cm are at the four corners of a square. Calculate the length of a diagonal of this square and hence find the radius of the smaller coin which, when placed at the centre of the square, touches the other four coins.

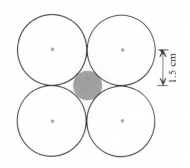

9

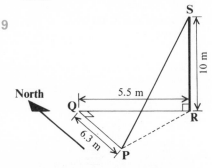

A vertical mast SR is 10 metres high and is fixed to the ground by a wire SP. P is 6.3 metres due south of Q and Q is 5.5 metres due west of R. Calculate the distances
a PR and   b PS,
giving the answers to the nearest 0.1 metre.

10 A mountain top M is 1.5 km above the town T. A ski-lift LM has its end L on the same level as the town and 2.4 km due west of the town.
If the point L is 1.8 km due north of the mountain MN, find
a   the length of the ski-lift LM
b   the distance of N from T and hence
c   the distance of M from T.

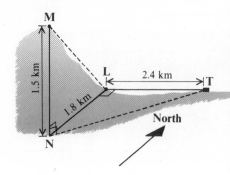

11

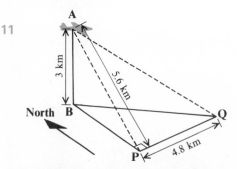

An aeroplane A is flying 3 km high when it is 5.6 km due north of point P. Point Q is 4.8 km due east of P. Calculate
a   the lengths BP and BQ
b   how far the aeroplane A is from Q.

12 A vertical mast PQ is supported by two wires AQ and BQ fixed to the ground at A and B 12.7 m apart so that angle APB is a right angle. If the wire AQ is 9.6 m long and the distance AP is 8.2 m, calculate
a   the height of the mast PQ
b   the distance PB
c   the length of the wire QB.

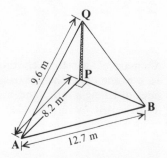

Pythagoras' theorem

13 Two walls of a room meet at XC
and the floor meets the two walls at
YC and ZC. A straight rod AB is
propped in the corner of the room
so that its lower end B is 3.1 m
from YC and 2.3 m from ZC. Its
upper end A is 2.5 m off the floor.
Calculate
a the distance CB
b the length of the rod AB.

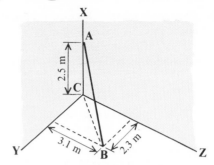

14

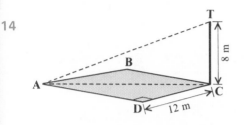

A square sports area $ABCD$ of side
12 m has a pole CT 8 m high in one
corner. Calculate
a the length of the diagonal AC
b the distance AT.

15 A vertical radio mast PQ is 15 m high and
anchored to the ground by four wires from Q
fixed to the corners of a square $WXYZ$ of side
11 m. Calculate
a the length of the diagonal WY
b the length WP
c the length of the wire WQ.

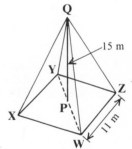

16 Find the lengths AC and AG in the following cuboids.

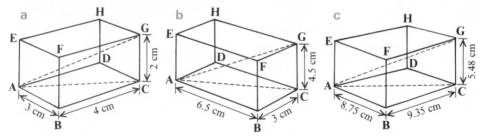

17 A box is 7 cm long, 5.3 cm wide and 4.4 cm high. Sketch the box and draw the
position of the longest possible straight rod which can be placed in the box.
Calculate the length of this rod.

18 Calculate the length of the longest possible straight rod which can be placed in a
box 7.7 cm long, 5.2 cm wide and 6.5 cm high.

19 A wedge has a cross-section ABC in
the shape of a right-angled triangle.
Given the lengths shown on the
diagram, calculate to the
nearest mm
a the length of the edge AC
b the length of the diagonal XB
c the length of the diagonal XC.

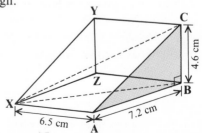

Pythagoras' theorem

20 Triangle *USP* is right-angled at *S*
and forms the cross-section of a
wedge. Given the lengths shown on
the diagram, calculate

a the length *SQ*   b the length *UQ*

c the area of triangle *USP*

d the volume of the wedge, to the
nearest whole cm^3

e the total surface area of the
wedge, to the nearest whole cm^2.

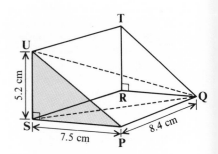

21

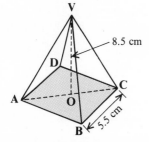

A pyramid has a square base *ABCD* of side
5.5 cm and a height *OV* of 8.5 cm where *O* is
the centre of the square base. Calculate

a the length *AC*

b the length *AO*

c the edge length *AV*.

22 A rectangular-based pyramid has
KL = 9.2 cm and *LM* = 7.4 cm.
If its slant edges are 8 cm long and
O is the centre of the base, calculate

a the length *KM*

b the length *OM*

c the height *OA*

d the volume of the pyramid to
the nearest cm^3.

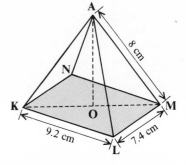

23

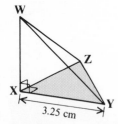

A tetrahedron is made from three identical
isosceles triangles, all having right angles meeting
at *X*. The fourth face is triangle *WYZ*.

a Calculate the length *WY*, if *XY* = 3.25 cm.

b What type of triangle is triangle *WYZ*?

24 A tetrahedron has three right-angled triangles as
faces, all meeting with their right angles at *B*.

a If *BC* = *BD* = 4.25 cm and *AC* = 7.75 cm,
calculate the lengths *DC* and *AB*.

b What kind of triangle is *ADC*? Sketch it
separately, writing on the lengths of its sides.

c If *M* is midpoint of *DC*, calculate the triangle's
height *AM* and its area.

d Find the total surface area of the tetrahedron.

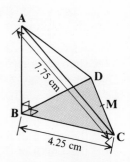

Pythagoras' theorem

Part 5 Pythagorean triples

1 The most well-known Pythagorean triple is $(3, 4, 5)$, and it can be used to make different triples (A, B, C) as this program shows.

10 LET $A = 3$: LET $B = 4$: LET $C = 5$

20 PRINT A, B, C

30 LET $X = A + 2$

40 LET $C = A + C + X$

50 LET $B = A + B + X$

60 LET $A = X$

70 GOTO 20

Copy and complete the table.

A	B	C	X	Print out
3	4	5		

In all the triples which you make, what do you notice about
a   the values of A as they increase
b   the values of $B + C$ compared with A^2
c   the values of $C - B$?

If you try this program on a computer, note that there is no END. You will need to find a way of breaking out of the loop between lines 20 to 70.

2 All possible Pythagorean triples (A, B, C) can be obtained from these formulae
$A = U^2 - V^2$
$B = 2UV$
$C = U^2 + V^2$

where U and V can have any integer values (with $U > V$), though it is best to have an even value for one and an odd value for the other.

Copy and complete this table where the values of U and V are given.

	U	V	A	B	C	A^2	B^2	$A^2 + B^2$	C^2
a	2	1							
b	3	2							
c	4	3							
d	5	4							
e	4	1							
f	5	2							
g	6	3							
h	7	4							
i	6	1							
j	7	2							

What do you notice about the Pythagorean triples if U and V are
k   both even   l   both odd?

Pythagoras' theorem

3   The $(3, 4, 5)$ and $(5, 12, 13)$ are the most common Pythagorean triples.

Are triangles with the following sides enlargements of the $(3, 4, 5)$ triangle, or the $(5, 12, 13)$ triangle, or neither of these?

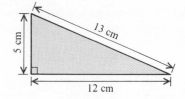

a	6 cm, 8 cm, 10 cm	b	10 cm, 24 cm, 26 cm
c	9 cm, 12 cm, 15 cm	d	15 cm, 36 cm, 40 cm
e	30 cm, 40 cm, 50 cm	f	25 cm, 60 cm, 65 cm
g	12 cm, 16 cm, 25 cm	h	20 cm, 48 cm, 50 cm
i	15 cm, 20 cm, 25 cm	j	18 cm, 24 cm, 30 cm
k	40 cm, 96 cm, 120 cm	l	$2\frac{1}{2}$ cm, 6 cm, $6\frac{1}{2}$ cm
m	$1\frac{1}{2}$ cm, 2 cm, $2\frac{1}{2}$ cm	n	1 cm, $2\frac{2}{5}$ cm, $2\frac{3}{5}$ cm
o	$4\frac{1}{2}$ cm, 6 cm, $7\frac{1}{2}$ cm	p	$\frac{3}{10}$ cm, $\frac{2}{5}$ cm, $\frac{1}{2}$ cm

The right-angled triangle

These problems involve Pythagoras' Theorem and the sine, cosine and tangent of angles.

1   Find the lettered lengths and angles in these triangles. Give the answers to three significant figures.

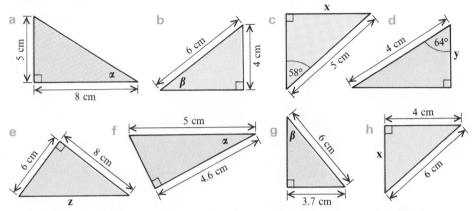

2   Find the lettered lengths and angles in these triangles. Give the answers to three significant figures.

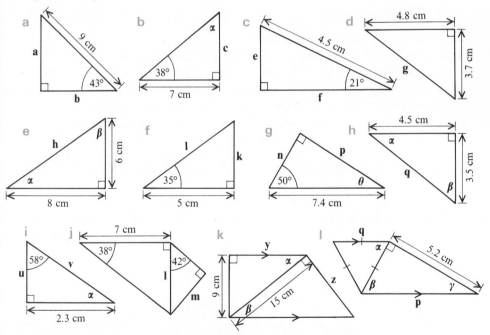

Draw diagrams for these problems and give the answers to three significant figures.

3   A ski-run 6 km long falls vertically through a height of 2 km. What angle does the run make with the horizontal?

4   A tree 12 metres tall casts a shadow 16 metres long onto level ground. Calculate the altitude of the sun.

5   A pipe 4 km long rises steadily at an angle of 6° to the horizontal. How much higher is the upper end of the pipe than the lower end?

The right-angled triangle

6　I walk 5 km due south and then 6 km due east. What is the shortest distance now between me and my starting point?

7　An aeroplane takes off and, after climbing gradually for a distance of 21 km, is 6 km high. Find the angle at which it is climbing.

8　A kite flies 48 metres high at the end of 180 metres of string. What angle does the string make with the horizontal?

9　A square has sides 12 cm long. What is the shortest distance between the midpoints of two adjacent sides?

10　A ladder 8 metres long leans against a vertical wall so that its foot is 3 metres from the base of the wall.
　a　How far up the wall does the ladder reach?
　b　What is the inclination of the ladder to the ground?

11　A hiker leaves a youth hostel and walks 4.5 km due north and then 6.3 km due east to reach a village.
　a　What is the shortest distance between the hostel and the village?
　b　What is the bearing of the village from the hostel (to the nearest degree)?

12　A rectangle is 5.5 cm long with diagonals 7.3 cm long. Find
　a　the length of its short sides　　　b　its area.

13　A circle, centre O and radius 10 cm, has a chord AB of length 9 cm.
　a　How far is the midpoint of the chord from O?
　b　What is the size of angle AOB?

14　A circle, centre O and radius 10 cm, has a chord CD such that angle COD is 150°. Calculate the length of the chord.

15　A goat is tied to a stake with a 10-metre rope which is 8 metres from a straight hedge. Find the length of hedge which the goat is able to reach.

16　An isosceles triangle ABC has $AB = AC = 7.2$ cm and $BC = 6.4$ cm. Calculate
　a　the height AM of the triangle where M is the midpoint of BC
　b　the area of the triangle　　　c　the three angles of the triangle.

17　The isosceles triangle XYZ has $XY = XZ = 8.2$ cm and angle $YXZ = 62°$. A line is drawn from Y to XZ to meet XZ at point P so that YP is perpendicular to XZ. Calculate　　a　the length YP　　　b　the area of triangle XYZ.

18　A rhombus has diagonals 12.4 cm and 8.8 cm. Calculate the length of its sides.

19　M is the midpoint of the side AB of the square $ABCD$. If AB is 16 cm long, find
　a　the length MD　　　b　the angle which MD makes with AD.

20

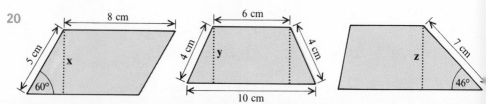

　a　A parallelogram has sides of 5 cm and 8 cm with an angle of 60° between them as shown. Calculate the height x of the parallelogram.
　b　An isosceles trapezium has parallel sides of 6 cm and 10 cm and two other sides of 4 cm. Calculate the height y of the trapezium.
　c　Another trapezium has a side of 7 cm at 46° to one of the parallel sides as shown. Calculate the height z of this trapezium.

The right-angled triangle

21 An isosceles right-angled triangle has a hypotenuse of 8 cm. What is the length of its other two sides?

22 *P* and *Q* are two points on the 900 m and 700 m contours of a hill. If they are separated horizontally by a distance of 30 m, calculate the angle of elevation α of *P* from *Q*.

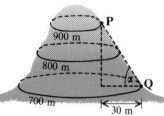

23

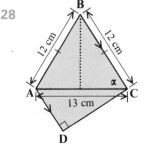

This map has a scale of 1 cm = 50 m and the contours on it are 20 m apart.
  a Use a ruler to find the horizontal distance between *R* and *S*.
  b How much higher is *R* than *S*?
  c Calculate the angle of elevation of *R* from *S*.

24 *Y* and *Z* are two points on a map with a scale of 1 cm = 250 m. If the contours are 50 m apart, find
  a the horizontal distance between *Y* and *Z*
  b the vertical distance between *Y* and *Z*
  c the angle of elevation of *Y* from *Z*.

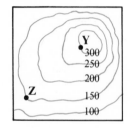

25 On graph paper draw and label the *x*- and *y*-axes from 0 to 8.
Join each of these pairs of points with a straight line.
For each line, write its gradient and use tables to find the angle it makes with the *x*-axis. Check the answers using a protractor.
  a (0, 0) and (1, 5)   b (1, 0) and (3, 8)
  c (2, 0) and (4, 6)   d (3, 0) and (7, 8)
  e (4, 0) and (8, 4)   f (5, 0) and (7, 1)

26 Draw and label the *x*- and the *y*-axes from −6 to 6.
Plot these pairs of points and calculate the shortest distance between them.
  a (3, 3) and (1, 6)   b (4, 2) and (5, 6)
  c (3, −2) and (6, 1)   d (2, −6) and (−4, −4)
  e (−5, −3) and (−2, 1)   f (−6, 5) and (1, 2)

27 For each of these vectors, calculate their length and the angle which they make with the direction of the *x*-axis.

  a $\begin{pmatrix} 3 \\ 4 \end{pmatrix}$ b $\begin{pmatrix} 8 \\ 6 \end{pmatrix}$ c $\begin{pmatrix} 3 \\ 8 \end{pmatrix}$ d $\begin{pmatrix} 4 \\ -5 \end{pmatrix}$ e $\begin{pmatrix} 5 \\ -8 \end{pmatrix}$ f $\begin{pmatrix} 9 \\ -6 \end{pmatrix}$

28

Triangle *ABC* is isosceles with *AB* = *BC* = 12 cm and *AC* = 13 cm. If *BC* is parallel to *AD*, calculate
  a angle α
  b the length *AD*
  c the length *DC*.

The right-angled triangle

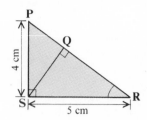

29 Given the lengths shown on the diagram,
calculate angle SRP and the lengths SQ, PQ
and RQ.

30

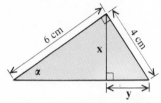

Calculate angle α and the lengths x and y.

31 A square $ABCD$ has sides of 4.5 cm. On the diagonal AC is drawn a larger
square $ACEF$. Find the length AC and the area of the square $ACEF$.

32 The playground of a primary school
is a square $ABCD$ of side 10 metres.
In corner C stands a flagpole CE
8 m high. Calculate
a the length AC
b the angle of elevation of the top
of the pole from corner B
c the angle of elevation of the top
of the pole from corner A.

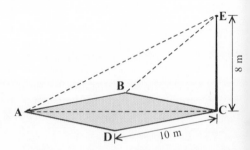

33

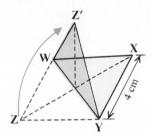

A horizontal square piece of paper $WXYZ$
of edge 4 cm is folded along its diagonal WY
and the corner Z is brought up to Z' so that
triangle WYZ' is vertical. Calculate
a the length of the diagonal XZ of the
square
b the distance between X and Z'
c the angle which XZ' makes with the
horizontal.

34 A metal coil has a vertical height of 5 cm. The length of
wire which makes the coil is 40 cm long.
Calculate the angle which the length of wire makes with
the horizontal.

35

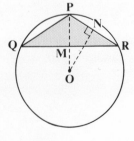

In triangle PQR, $PQ = PR = 15$ cm and
$QR = 20$ cm. M and N are the midpoints of
sides QR and PR and O is the circumcentre of the
triangle. Calculate
a angle MPR
b the radius of the circle.

Further Topics

Bearings

Part 1

Sketch a diagram for each problem before making any calculations.
Give distances where necessary to three significant figures and bearings to the nearest whole degree.

1   Upleadon is 4 miles due west of Hasfield and Redmarley is 3 miles due north of Upleadon. Find the shortest distance from Hasfield to Redmarley.

2   Tadcaster is 6 miles due north of Sherburn and Osgodby is 8 miles due east of Sherburn. Find the distance direct from Tadcaster to Osgodby.

3   Ingoldsby is 2 miles due south of Humby and Aslackby is 4 miles due east of Ingoldsby. What is the shortest distance between Aslackby and Humby?

4   Dinas is 6.5 km due west of Caer and is also 7.2 km due north of Mynydd. Calculate the distance direct from Caer to Mynydd.

5   Kilbryde is 8 km due north of Glenend and Dunmuir is 5 km due east of Kilbryde. Find
    a   the shortest distance from Dunmuir to Glenend.
    b   the bearing of Dunmuir from Glenend.

6   Ullscar is 7 km due east of Strands and Yargyll is 4 km due south of Strands. Find
    a   the distance direct from Ullscar to Yargyll
    b   the bearing of Ullscar from Yargyll.

7   Ford is 4.5 km due south of Duddo and Bowsden is 7.2 km due east of Duddo. Calculate
    a   the shortest distance between Bowsden and Ford
    b   the bearing of Bowsden from Ford.

8   Lochurr is 2.8 km due east of Craigend and Brogie is 4 km due north of Craigend. Find
    a   the shortest distance between Lochurr and Brogie
    b   the bearing of Lochurr from Brogie.

9   Monkton is 7.2 km due east of Shadwell and Hutton is 8 km due north of Shadwell.
    a   What is the direct distance from Monkton to Hutton?
    b   On what bearing is Monkton from Hutton?

10 Nateby is 4.5 miles due north of Inskip and Elswick is 3.6 miles due west of Inskip. Calculate the bearing of Elswick from Nateby.

11 Thornhill is 2.4 miles due west of Horbury and Bretton is 2.7 miles due south of Horbury. What is the bearing of Thornhill from Bretton?

12 Burry is 3.2 miles due west of Llanelli and Oxwich is 7.2 miles due south of Llanelli. On what bearing is Burry from Oxwich?

13 Cambourne is 9 miles from Marazion on a bearing of 052°. St Ives is due west of Cambourne and due north of Marazion.
    Calculate the shortest distance between
    a   St Ives and Cambourne   b   St Ives and Marazion.

14 Ashford is 37 miles from Eastbourne on a bearing of 048°. Tunbridge Wells is due north of Eastbourne and also due west of Ashford.
    Calculate the shortest distance between
    a   Tunbridge Wells and Ashford   b   Tunbridge Wells and Eastbourne.

Bearings

15 Widnes is 12 miles from Bootle on a bearing of 120°. St Helens is due east of
Bootle and also due north of Widnes.
Calculate the distance between
a Bootle and St Helens   b St Helens and Widnes.

16 Unterham is 7.5 km from Linksby on a bearing of 125°. Mittleton is due east of
Linksby and due north of Unterham.
Calculate the distance between
a Mittleton and Linksby   b Mittleton and Unterham.

17 An aircraft flies 40 km on a bearing of 222°. How far has it flown
a to the west   b to the south?

18 A ship steams 52 km on a bearing of 325°. How far has it travelled
a to the west   b to the north?

Part 2

Sketch a diagram for each problem before making any calculations.
Give distances where necessary to three significant figures and bearings to the nearest
whole degree.

1 Askham A is 6 km from Boston B on a bearing of 020°.
Culham C is 8 km from Boston B on a bearing of 110°. Find
a angle ABC   b the distance from Askham to Culham.

2 Tunworth T is 5 km from Compton C on a bearing of 040°.
Holditch H is 7 km from Compton C on a bearing of 130°. Find
a angle TCH   b the distance between Tunworth and Holditch.

3 Longrave L is 6.8 km from Okeford O on a bearing of 135°.
Pendly P is 7.2 km from Okeford O on a bearing of 225°. Find
a angle POL   b the distance between Pendly and Longrave.

4 Toller T is 8.1 km from Bobwick B on a bearing of 170°.
Drayton D is on a bearing of 260° from Bobwick B.
a Find angle DBT.
b If Toller and Drayton are 9.4 km apart, how far apart are Drayton and
Bobwick?

5 Milden M is 5.2 km from Rowbridge R on a bearing of 070°.
Heywood H is on a bearing of 340° from Rowbridge. If Heywood and Milden
are 7.6 km apart, find
a angle HRM   b the distance between Heywood and Rowbridge.

6 Pately P is on a bearing of 024° from Donhill D and Witham W is on a
bearing of 294° from Donhill D. Pately is 10 miles from Witham and 6.4 miles
from Donhill. Find
a angle WDP   b the distance between Witham and Donhill.

7 Two ships A and B leave the harbour H with ship A on a bearing of 300° and
ship B on a bearing of 210°. After ship A has travelled 7.8 km and ship B
5.2 km, what is
a angle AHB   b the distance AB between them?

8 Ship Y leaves port P on a bearing of 143° at the same time as ship Z leaves P
on a bearing of 233°. The two ships are 9.1 km apart when Y is 5.6 km from P.
Calculate
a angle YPZ   b how far Z is from P.

141

Bearings

9   Awley A is 18 km from Budmouth B on a bearing of 070°.
Carnton C is 10 km from Budmouth B on a bearing of 160°. Find
a   angle ABC b   angle BCA
c   the bearing of Awley from Carnton.

10   Elkham E is 8 miles from Fenton F on a bearing of 085°.
Gilforth G is 5 miles from Fenton F on a bearing of 175°. Find
a   angle EFG b   angle FGE
c   the bearing of Elkham from Gilforth.

11   Johnston J is 14 km from Higham H on a bearing of 120°.
Immingby I is 20 km from Higham H on a bearing of 210°. Find
a   angle IHJ b   angle HIJ
c   the bearing of Johnston from Immingby.

12   Littleham L is 10 miles from Marsh M on a bearing of 165°.
Kingston K is 16 miles from Marsh M on a bearing of 255°. Find
a   angle KML b   angle MKL
c   the bearing of Littleham from Kingston.

13   Althorpe A is 6 km from Bamwith B on a bearing of 330°.
Cumberton C is on a bearing of 060° from B and also on a bearing of 080°
from A. Calculate
a   angle ABC b   angle BAC c   the distance BC.

14   Two hikers leave the Youth Hostel H at the same time. Steve S leaves on a
bearing of 050° and Terry T leaves on a bearing of 140°. When Terry has gone
3 km he can see Steve on a bearing of 020°. Calculate
a   angle SHT b   angle HTS c   how far Steve has gone
d   the distance between Terry and Steve.

15   From where I am standing I can see a water-tower W on a bearing of 235° and
a TV mast M on a bearing of 145°. If the tower and mast are 12 km apart and
the bearing of M from W is 070°, find
a   angle MIW b   angle IWM
c   how far I am from the tower   d   how far I am from the mast.

16   Ship A leaves harbour H on a bearing of 035° and ship B leaves H on a bearing
of 125°. When the ships are 24 miles apart, ship A is 9 miles from H. Calculate
a   angle AHB b   angle HAB c   the bearing of B from A.

17   Canisp C is 3 miles from Suilven S on a bearing of 085°.
Cul Mor M is 4 miles from Suilven on a bearing of 175°. Find
a   angle CSM b   angle SMC
c   the bearing of Canisp from Cul Mor to the nearest degree
d   the distance between Canisp and Cul Mor.

18   Northleach N is 21 km from Moreton M on a bearing of 205°.
Broadway B is 12 km from Moreton on a bearing of 295°. Find
a   angle BMN b   the bearing of Moreton from Broadway
c   angle BNM
d   the bearing of Moreton from Northleach to the nearest degree
e   the distance between Broadway and Northleach.

Part 3

Sketch a diagram for each problem before making any calculations. Give the answers to three significant figures where necessary.

1   I leave point *A* and walk 5 km on a bearing of 050° to reach point *B*.
    How far is
    a   *B* to the east of *A*   b   *B* to the north of *A*?

    I now leave *B* and walk 6.4 km on a bearing of 120° to reach point *C* which is due east of *A*. How far is
    c   *C* to the east of *B*   d   *C* to the south of *B*   e   *A* from *C*?

2   A fishing boat leaves harbour *H* and sails 7.5 km on a bearing of 065° to reach a buoy *B*. How far is
    a   *B* to the east of *H*   b   *B* to the north of *H*?

    The boat leaves *B* and sails a further 4.1 km on a bearing of 140° to reach a lighthouse *L* which is due east of *H*. How far is
    c   *L* to the east of *B*   d   *L* to the south of *B*   e   *H* from *L*?

3   A power station *P* supplies electricity to a village *A* by a line which runs the 5 km from *P* to *A* on a bearing of 037°. How far is
    a   *A* to the east of *P*   b   *A* to the north of *P*?

    A second village *B* is now supplied from *A* by a line 6 km long, running from *A* to *B* on a bearing of 330°. How far is *B*
    c   west of *A*   d   north of *A*?
    e   In which direction is *B* from *P*, and how far apart are *B* and *P*?

4   A yacht sails 5 km on a bearing of 025° from point *X* to point *Y*, before it changes direction to sail another 5 km from *Y* to *Z* on a new bearing of 065°. Sketch this diagram and put all the information given onto it. How far is
    a   *Y* to the east of *X*
    b   *Z* to the east of *Y*
    c   *Z* to the east of *X*
    d   *Y* to the north of *X*
    e   *Z* to the north of *Y*
    f   *Z* to the north of *X*?
    g   Use Pythagoras' Theorem to calculate the shortest distance between *X* and *Z*.

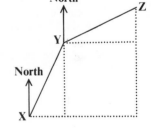

5   A light aircraft leaves Plymouth for Birmingham 300 km away on a bearing of 030°. It then leaves Birmingham for London which is 150 km away on a bearing of 140°. How far is
    a   Birmingham to the east of Plymouth
    b   London to the east of Plymouth
    c   Birmingham to the north of Plymouth
    d   London to the north of Plymouth?
    e   Use Pythagoras' Theorem to find the direct distance from London to Plymouth.
    f   If the aircraft averages a speed of 200 km/h, how long did it take for the trip?
    g   If it returns direct from London to Plymouth, how long will it take at the same average speed?

Bearings

6 A fishing boat leaves Dublin and sails 150 km on a bearing of 055° to reach Douglas on the Isle of Man. It then sails 100 km from Douglas on a bearing of 105° to reach Fleetwood. How far is
  a Douglas to the east of Dublin
  b Fleetwood to the east of Dublin
  c Douglas to the north of Dublin
  d Fleetwood to the north of Dublin?
  e Use Pythagoras' Theorem to find the shortest distance from Dublin to Fleetwood.
  f If the boat averages a speed of 20 km/h, how long did the whole journey take?
  g If it had gone direct to Fleetwood from Dublin, how much shorter in time would the journey have been?

7 A, B and C are three airfields, with B 100 km due north of A. C is 50 km from A on a bearing of 052°. Sketch their relative positions. Calculate
  a how much further north C is than A
  b how much further east C is than A
  c how much further north B is than C
  d the distance between B and C
  e the bearing of C from B to the nearest degree.

  Two aircraft set off from A and B at the same time and they land at C at the same time.
  f Which aircraft is the faster?
  g If the one from A had an average speed of 500 km/h, how long did it take to reach C and what was the average speed of the other plane?

8 A hiker walks 6 km on a bearing of 040° and then turns onto a new bearing of 110° to walk a further 5 km.
  a Sketch a diagram showing his route.
  b Calculate his total eastward distance covered.
  c Calculate his total northward distance covered.
  d What is the shortest distance between his starting and finishing points?

Latitude and longitude

Part 1

A model

Cut out of thin card three circles each with a radius of 5 cm. Cut slots of 5 cm or $2\frac{1}{2}$ cm in the circles as shown.

Fold four flaps gently along the four dotted lines and bring circles A and B together by sliding slots 1 and 2 along each other.

Slide the cross-shaped slot of circle C over the four folded flaps of A and B and then straighten the folded flaps to complete the model.

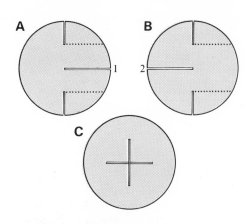

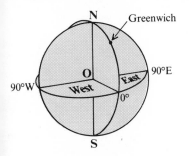

A quadrant of radius 5 cm, on which angle λ denotes the *latitude* of point X, can be cut out and placed in the model. When rotated about ON, the angle of rotation from the Greenwich Meridian illustrates the *longitude* of point X.

1   Five circles are drawn on the surface of this globe.
Which of them are
a   great circles
b   small circles?

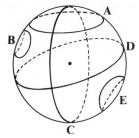

2   These two diagrams illustrate *meridians* and *parallels of latitude*.
NP and SP indicate the North Pole and South Pole.

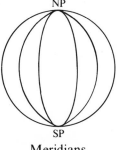

Meridians

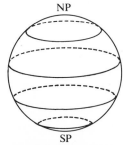

Parallels of latitude

a   Is every meridian a great circle? Answer *yes* or *no*.

b   What are the names of the two points at which all meridians intersect each other?

c   What is the name of the meridian which passes through part of London?

145

Latitude and longitude

d Is every parallel of latitude a great circle? Answer *yes* or *no*.

e Is every parallel of latitude a small circle? Answer *yes* or *no*.

f How many of the parallels of latitude are great circles?

g What is the name given to the only parallel of latitude which is also a great circle?

h What can you say about the meridian 180°E and 180°W?

i What is the name of the place with a latitude of 90°N?

j What is the name of the place with a latitude of 90°S?

k What is the name given to the parallel of latitude 0°?

l What name is given to the line which runs from the North Pole to the South Pole through the Pacific Ocean, following for most of its length the meridian 180°E?

3 This diagram shows that the two meridians 20°E and 160°W together make a great circle.

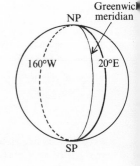

Which other meridian will make a great circle with

a	the meridian 30°E	b	the meridian 50°E
c	the meridian 90°E	d	the meridian 140°E
e	the meridian 20°W	f	the meridian 60°W
g	the meridian 100°W	h	the meridian 170°W
i	the meridian 80°E	j	the meridian 5°E
k	the meridian 25°W	l	the meridian 180°E?

4

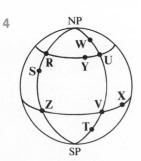

This diagram shows two meridians and two parallels of latitude.

Name all the points on the diagram which have

a the same latitude as *Y*

b the same latitude as *V*

c the same longitude as *W*

d the same longitude as *Z*.

5 Name all the points on this diagram which have

a the same latitude as *A*

b the same longitude as *G*

c the same latitude as *G*.

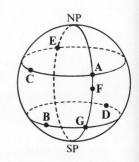

Latitude and longitude

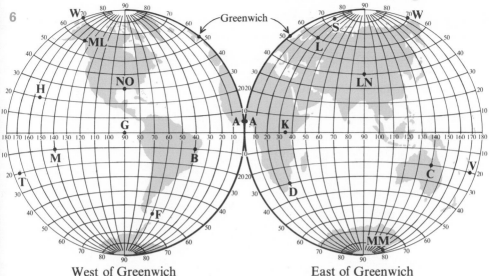

West of Greenwich   East of Greenwich

Remembering that parallels of lAtitude go Across the earth
and meridians of lOngitude go Over the pOles,
write the latitude and longitude for these places (indicated by initials on the diagram).

a	Leningrad *L*	b	Lop Nor *LN*	c	Durban *D*
d	Cloncurry *C*	e	New Orleans *NO*	f	Mount Logan *ML*
g	Falkland Islands *F*	h	Svalbard *S*	i	Bahia *B*
j	Vanuatu *V*	k	Tonga *T*	l	Accra *A*
m	Kisumu *K*	n	Galapagos Islands *G*	o	Hawaii *H*
p	Mount Markham *MM*	q	Marquesas Islands *M*	r	Wrangel Island *W*

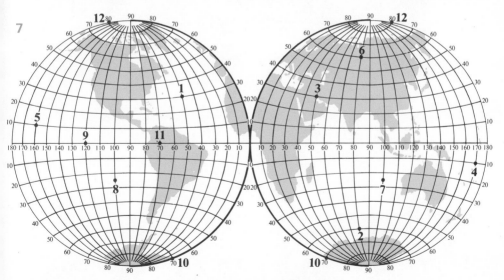

This diagram shows the whole surface area of the earth.
Match the numbers on the diagram with the letters of the places listed here.

a	(30°N 50°W)	b	(30°N 50°E)	c	(60°S 80°E)	d	(60°N 80°E)
e	(10°N 160°W)	f	(10°S 170°E)	g	(0° 120°W)	h	(25°S 100°W)
i	(25°S 100°E)	j	(80°N 180°E)	k	(0° 70°W)	l	(70°S 0°)

Latitude and longitude

8 This diagram shows half of the surface area of the earth.

Match the numbers on the diagram with the letters of the places listed here.

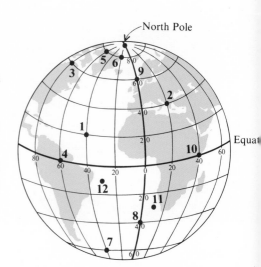

a (40°N 20°E) b (80°N 20°W)

c (60°S 40°W) d (0° 60°W)

e (0° 40°E) f (60°N 80°W)

g (60°N 0°) h (20°N 40°W)

i (80°N 60°W) j (30°S 10°E)

k (10°S 30°W) l (40°S 0°)

9

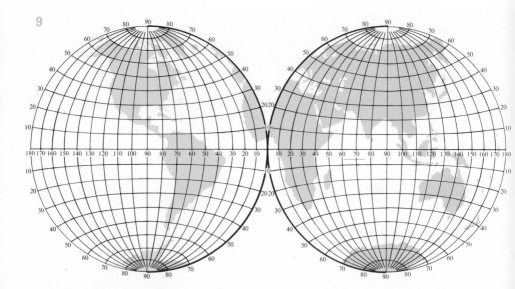

This diagram shows the whole surface area of the earth.

Either use tracing paper to copy this diagram

or use any similar diagram and on the copy mark each of these points with its letter.

a (30°N 50°E) b (60°N 40°W) c (20°S 160°W)

d (70°S 90°E) e (80°N 80°E) f (70°S 10°W)

g (0° 10°W) h (0° 120°E) i (50°N 170°E)

j (60°N 0°) k (40°S 0°) l (0° 100°W)

m (50°N 165°W) n (75°S 140°W) o (0° 0°)

Latitude and longitude

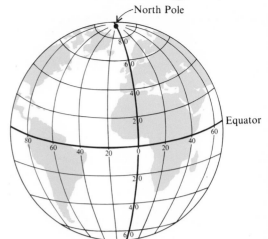

10 This diagram shows half of the surface of the earth.

Either use tracing paper to copy this diagram
or use any similar diagram and on the copy mark each of these points with its letter.

a (20°N 40°E)   b (20°S 60°E)
c (60°N 10°W)   d (20°S 80°W)
e (40°S 20°W)   f (40°S 20°E)
g (0° 40°W)   h (0° 30°E)
i (20°N 0°)   j (60°S 0°)
k (80°N 10°W)   l (50°N 70°W)

11 The diagram in question 9 will be useful when answering these problems.
Write the latitude and longitude of the point you arrive at if you leave the point
a (10°N 20°E) and travel 40° due north
b (20°N 30°W) and travel 30° due north
c (10°N 90°E) and travel 50° due south
d (30°N 100°W) and travel 40° due south
e (10°N 20°E) and travel 10° due east
f (20°S 50°E) and travel 20° due east
g (40°S 10°E) and travel 30° due west
h (50°N 20°E) and travel 50° due west
i (10°S 140°E) and travel 60° due south
j (30°N 130°W) and travel 40° due north
k (50°S 90°E) and travel 100° due north
l (0° 120°W) and travel 200° due east
m (0° 170°E) and travel 200° due west
n (0° 150°W) and travel 160° due east
o (40°N 80°W) and travel 30° due south
p (70°S 120°E) and travel 60° due north
q (0° 150°W) and travel 30° due west
r (0° 170°E) and travel 20° due east
s (10°N 100°W) and travel 90° due west
t (20°S 140°E) and travel 60° due east.

12 Write the latitude and longitude of the point you reach if you leave the point
a (30°N 10°E) and go 20° due north and then 50° due east
b (20°S 30°E) and go 40° due south and then 100° due east
c (50°N 40°W) and go 10° due south and then 60° due west
d (10°N 60°W) and go 30° due south and then 100° due west
e (50°S 10°E) and go 70° due north and then 20° due east
f (70°N 80°E) and go 10° due south and then 90° due west
g (30°S 5°W) and go 40° due south and then 25° due east
h (10°N 0°) and go 80° due south and then 40° due west
i (50°S 0°) and go 90° due north and then 120° due east
j (0° 120°W) and go 30° due south and then 40° due west
k (50°N 150°E) and go 10° due north and then 30° due east
l (70°S 140°W) and go 80° due north and then 50° due west.

149

Latitude and longitude

13 X and Y are two points on the earth's surface
    such that the line XOY is a diameter of the earth,
    where O is the centre of the earth. Find the
    position of X if Y is the point

a (40°N 30°E)   b (70°N 60°E)

c (70°N 100°E)   d (30°S 120°E)

e (50°S 10°W)   f (20°S 80°W)

g (75°S 160°W)   h (35°N 145°E).

The remaining problems in this part are *multiple-choice* questions.

Select the one correct answer from the choices offered.

14 Cayenne (5°N 52°W) in South America and Monrovia (5°N 11°W) in West
    Africa are both capital cities. The difference in their longitudes is
    a 0°   b 41°   c 10°   d 63°.

15 Timbuktu (16°N 3°W) and Khartoum (16°N 33°E) are both African cities.
    The difference in their longitudes is
    a 0°   b 36°   c 32°   d 30°.

16 London ($51\frac{1}{2}$°N 0°) and Accra ($5\frac{1}{2}$°N 0°) both lie on the Greenwich Meridian.
    The difference in their latitudes is
    a 0°   b 57°   c 46°   d 47°.

17 What is the difference in the latitudes of these two Australian cities,
    Melbourne (38°S 145°E) and Cooktown (15°S 145°E)?
    a 0°   b 53°   c 23°   d 33°

18 What is the difference in the longitudes of Cape Town (34°S 19°E) in South
    Africa and Montevideo (34°S 56°W) in South America?
    s 0°   b 34°   c 75°   d 38°

19 Find the difference in the latitudes of Budapest (48°N 19°E) in Hungary and
    Cape Town (34°S 19°E) in South Africa.
    a 0°   b 19°   c 14°   d 82°

20 Bellinzona (46.2°N 9°E) is in Switzerland and Eberbach (49.5°N 9°E) is in
    Germany. The difference in their longitudes is
    a 0°   b 18°   c 3.3°   d 95.7°.

21 The two Pacific islands of Fiji (18°S 175°E) and Tahiti (18°S 150°W) have
    a difference in their longitudes of
    a 0°   b 36°   c 28°   d 35°.

22 The islands of Samoa (12°S 170°W) and Rotuma (12°S 177°E) have
    a difference in their longitudes of
    a 0°   b 5°   c 13°   d 12°.

23 The shortest route from A (0° 45°E) to B (30°N 45°E) is
    a along the equator   b along the Greenwich Meridian
    c via the North Pole   d along the meridian 45°E.

24 The shortest route from C (0° 25°W) to D (0° 65°E) is
    a along the equator   b along the Greenwich Meridian
    c via the North Pole   d along the meridian 65°E.

25 The shortest distance from E (80°N 0°) to F (80°N 180°W) is
    a along the equator   b along the parallel of latitude 80°N
    c via the North Pole   d via the South Pole.

Latitude and longitude

26 The shortest distance between Quito (0° 78°W) in Ecuador and
Nanyuki (0° 37°E) in Kenya is
   a   along the Greenwich Meridian   b   over the South Pole
   c   along the equator   d   none of these.

27 The shortest distance from Anchorage (61°N 150°W) in Alaska to
Imatra (61°N 30°E) in Finland is
   a   along the parallel of latitude 61°N   b   over the North Pole
   c   over the South Pole   d   none of these.

28 The shortest distance from Tashkent (41°N 68°E) in USSR to Salt Lake City
(41°N 112°W) in USA is
   a   along the parallel of latitude 41°N   b   via the equator
   c   over the North Pole   d   none of these.

29 The points Y (0° 30°W) and Z (0° 30°E) both lie on the equator. Which one of
these four points is equal distance from Y and from Z?
   a   (0° 60°E)   b   (60°N 0°)   c   (30°N 30°E)   d   (30°S 30°W)

30 The points L (0° 90°W) and M (0° 150°W) both lie on the equator. Which one
of these four points is equidistant from L and M?
   a   (50°S 120°W)   b   (0° 90°E)   c   (0° 120°E)   d   (10°N 150°W)

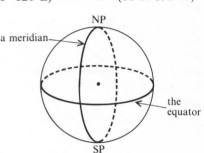

Part 2   Great circles

A great circle is the largest possible circle
which can be drawn on the earth's surface.

The centre of a great circle is also the centre of
the earth.

The equator and all meridians are great circles.

1 Take the radius of the earth as 6370 km.
Sketch the positions of these places on a diagram and use logarithms or a
calculator to find the distances between them. Give the answers to three
significant figures.

   a   Entebbe (0° 32°E) and Libreville (0° 9°E)
   b   Galapagos Islands (0° 90°W) and Quito (0° 78°W)
   c   Sumatra (0° 99°E) and the Somali coast (0° 42°E)
   d   Across the Atlantic Ocean from the Congolese coast (0° 9°E) to the mouth of
the Amazon (0° 49°W)
   e   Between the snow-capped peaks of Mount Kenya (0° $37\frac{1}{2}$°E) and
Cotopaxi (0° $78\frac{1}{2}$°W)
   f   New Orleans (30°N 90°W) and St Louis (38°N 90°W)
   g   Aden (13°N 45°E) and Baghdad (33°N 45°E)
   h   London ($51\frac{1}{2}$°N 0°) and Accra ($5\frac{1}{2}$°N 0°) in Ghana
   i   Moscow (56°N 38°E) and Moshi (3°S 38°E) in Tanzania
   j   Adelaide (35°S 139°E) and Tokyo (36°N 139°E)
   k   Across Africa from the Atlantic Ocean at (0° 9°E) to the Indian Ocean at
(0° 43°E)
   l   Across South America from the Atlantic Ocean at (0° 50°W) to the Pacific
Ocean at (0° 80°W)
   m   Oslo (60°N 10°E) in Norway to Tunis (37°N 10°E) in North Africa
   n   Stockholm (59°N 18°E) in Sweden and Cape Town (34°S 18°E) in South
Africa

Latitude and longitude

2 An aeroplane flies direct from John o' Groats (58.6°N 3°W) to Cardiff (51.4°N 3°W) at a steady speed of 200 km/h. Calculate
  a the distance it travels   b the time it takes.

3 An aeroplane flies direct from Montreal ($45\frac{1}{2}$°N 74°W) in Canada to New York (41°N 74°W) in USA at an average speed of 250 km/h. Find
  a the distance between these two cities   b the time taken by the aeroplane.

4 A holiday charter flight travels from Edinburgh (56°N 4°W) to Malaga (38°N 4°W) at an average speed of 500 km/h. Calculate how long the flight is
  a in kilometres   b in hours.

5 The Gilbert Islands (0° 173°E) and the Galapagos Islands (0° 91°W) both lie on the equator in the Pacific Ocean on opposite sides of the International Date Line. Calculate
  a the shortest distance between them
  b how long a ship would take to make the journey if it averaged 200 km per day.

6 How far is it from London ($51\frac{1}{2}$°N 0°) to the North Pole?

Part 3 Small circles

All parallels of latitude, except the equator, are small circles.

Point A has a latitude λ and triangle OCA demonstrates that the radius of the parallel of latitude r is given by $r = R \cos \lambda$, where R is the radius of the earth.

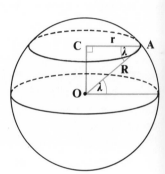

1 Take R as 6370 km and calculate the radius of the parallel of latitude r when
  a $\lambda = 20°$ b $\lambda = 54°$ c $\lambda = 68°$.
Give the answers to three significant figures.

2 Sketch the positions of these places on a diagram and use logarithms or a calculator to find the distances between them. Give the answers to three significant figures.
  a Leningrad (60°N 30°E) and Okhotsk (60°N 143°E) in USSR
  b Tehran (36°N 51°E) and Tokyo (36°N 140°E)
  c Vienna ($48\frac{1}{2}$°N 17°E) and Munich ($48\frac{1}{2}$°N 11°E)
  d Warsaw (52°N 21°E) and Evesham (52°N 2°W)
  e Moscow (56°N 38°E) and Berwick-on-Tweed (56°N 2°W)
  f Bathurst (13°N 17°W) and Aden (13°N 45°E)
  g Gloucester (52°N 2°W) and Rotterdam (52°N $4\frac{1}{2}$°E)
  h Across the Atlantic Ocean from Oporto (41°N 8°W) in Portugal to New York (41°N 74°W)
  i Across Australia from Perth (32°S 116°E) to Newcastle (32°S 152°E)
  j Along the Canada–US border from (49°N 126°W) to (49°N 95°W)
  k Across England and Wales from Fishguard (52°N 5°W) on the Irish Sea to Felixstowe (52°N $1\frac{1}{2}$°E) on the North Sea.
  l Across Ireland from Tralee (52.3°N 9.7°W) to Rosslare (52.3°N 6.3°W)

3 The shortest distance between Osaka ($34\frac{1}{2}$°N 136°E) in Japan and Los Angeles ($34\frac{1}{2}$°N 119°W) in California is across the Pacific Ocean and the International Date Line. Calculate the distance between these two cities along the parallel of latitude.

Latitude and longitude

4 Calculate the distance from Buenos Aires ($34\frac{1}{2}$°S 59°W) in Argentina to Wollongong ($34\frac{1}{2}$°S 151°E) in Australia along the parallel of latitude
  a across the Atlantic and Indian Oceans   b across the Pacific Ocean.

5 South Georgia (54°S 36°W) and Macquarie Island (54°S 160°E) are islands in the Southern Ocean. Find the distance between them along the parallel of latitude
  a on a route which crosses the Greenwich Meridian
  b on a route which crosses the International Date Line.

6 Draw a diagram to illustrate these three routes from Salt Lake City (41°N 112°W) in USA to Tashkent (41°N 68°E) in USSR.
  (i)   via the North Pole
  (ii) along the parallel of latitude and across the Greenwich Meridian
  (iii) along the parallel of latitude and across the International Date Line

  a Which one of these three routes is a great circle route?
  b Which two of these three routes are the same distance?
  c Which one of these three routes has the shortest distance?
  d Calculate the distance of route (ii) along the parallel of latitude.
  e Calculate the distance of route (i) via the North Pole.

Part 4 Nautical miles

A nautical mile is the distance on the earth's surface which makes an angle of 1 minute ($1' = \frac{1}{60}$°) at the centre of the earth. So, 60 n.m. will make an angle of 1° at the centre of the earth.

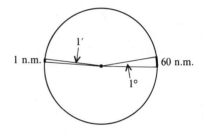

1 Find the distance (in n.m.) along the great circles which a ship sails when travelling between these pairs of points.

  a (0° 55°E), (0° 59°E)   b (0° 10°W), (0° 22°W)
  c (0° 84°W), (0° 99°W)   d (5°S 20°W), (21°S 20°W)
  e (34°S 80°E), (61°S 80°E)   f (24°N 160°E), (49°N 160°E)
  g (0° 2°E), (0° 3°W)   h (0° 9°E), (0° 41°W)
  i (26°N 15°W), (2°S 15°W)   j (23°N 120°W), (38°N 120°W)
  k (7°N 95°E), (41°S 95°E)   l (0° 172°E), (0° 179°W)

A speed of 1 nautical mile per hour is called *1 knot*.

2 A ship sails due north from the Isle of Lewis (58°N 7°W) in Scotland at a speed of 20 knots to reach the Faeroe Islands (62°N 7°W). Find
  a the distance travelled   b the time taken.

3 A yacht leaves the Irish coast at (52°N 8°W) and sails due south to reach the coast of Spain at (43°N 8°W). If it averages a speed of 12 knots, calculate
  a the distance travelled   b the time taken.

4 A pleasure craft crosses the Mediterranean Sea from Leghorn (43°N 10°E) in Italy to Tunis (37°N 10°E) in North Africa. Given that it maintains a speed of 18 knots, find
  a the length of the journey   b the time taken.

5 A steamer travels north from Ascension Island (8°S 14°W) in the Atlantic Ocean to reach the West African coast at (10°N 14°W) after 54 hours. Calculate
  a the distance travelled   b the average speed of the steamer in knots.

Latitude and longitude

6 The journey between the islands of Socotra (12°N 55°E) and the Seychelles (4°S 55°E) in the Indian Ocean takes a ship 40 hours.
   a Find the distance between these islands.
   b What is the average speed of the ship?

7 An arab dhow leaves the African coast at (0° 43°E) and sails due east along the equator averaging a speed of 10 knots.
   a How far has it to sail to reach the point (0° 51°E)?
   b How long will it take?

8 A ship crosses the Java Sea from Sumatra (0° 104°E) to Borneo (0° 109°E) taking 20 hours for the journey.
   a How far does the ship travel?   b What is its average speed in knots?

9 Sailing due west from the island of São Tomé (0° 7°E), a ship reaches the point (0° 17°W) in the Atlantic Ocean after 120 hours.
   a What distance has the ship travelled?
   b What was its average speed (in knots)?

10 Find the distance (in n.m.) along the *small* circles which a ship sails when travelling between these points. Give answers to three significant figures.
   a (20°S 60°E), (20°S 70°E)   b (40°S 35°E), (40°S 27°E)
   c (45°N 104°W), (45°N 145°W)   d (60°N 2°E), (60°N 10°W)
   e (53°S 8°W), (53°S 7°E)   f (4°N 176°W), (4°N 177°E)
   g (8°S 169°E), (8°S 178°W)   h (11°N 6°E), (11°N 32°W)

11 A cruiser sets sail due west from the coast of Portugal at (38°N 9°W) for its destination on the islands of the Azores (38°N 26°W) in the Atlantic Ocean.
   a How far has it to sail?   b How long will it take at a speed of 20 knots?

12 If a ship steams due east from the Newfoundland coast (50°N 55°W) in Canada, it will eventually arrive in Cornwall, England at (50°N 5°W).
   a What is the distance travelled?
   b How long will it take at an average speed of 15 knots?

13 A ship sails around Antarctica on the parallel of latitude 60°S at an average speed of 24 knots.
   a What is the length of this parallel (in nautical miles)?
   b How long does the ship take (in days and hours)?

14 An aircraft flies round the North Pole on the parallel of latitude 85°N at a speed of 400 knots. Find
   a the length of this parallel (in n.m.)
   b the time taken (in hours).

15 A ship steams from Valparaiso (33°S 72°W) in Chile and travels due west to reach New Zealand on the meridian 174°E. If its average speed is 18 knots, find the time taken (in days and hours).

16 Leaving the Canary Islands (28°N 16°W), a steamer travels at 15 knots due north to reach Iceland on the parallel 64°N. How long does the journey take?

17 Find the latitude and longitude of the second city from the information given.
   a Durban (30°S 32°E) is 720 n.m. due south of Harare.
   b Singapore (1°N 102°E) is 3180 n.m. due south of Irkutsk.
   c Lucknow (27°N 81°E) is 840 n.m. due north of Madras.
   d Nanyuki (0° 37°E) is 1080 n.m. due east of Mbandaka.

18 How far (in n.m.) is London ($51\frac{1}{2}$°N 0°) from the North Pole?

Introducing three dimensions

Part 1   Angles between two lines

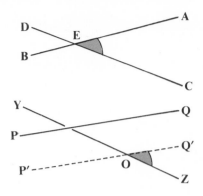

(i)   When the two lines *AB* and *CD* intersect at point *E*, the angle between the lines is ∠*AEC*.

(ii)   When the two lines *PQ* and *YZ* do *not* intersect and are *not* parallel, they are said to be **skew lines**. Imagine *PQ* moving parallel to itself until *P'Q'* intersects *YZ* at *O*. The angle between the lines *PQ* and *YZ* is ∠*Q'OZ*.

iii)   Two lines in three dimensions will
   either intersect
       or be parallel
       or be skew.

1

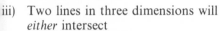

You are standing at one end of a room, looking towards the other end.

Do these pairs of lines intersect, are they parallel or are they skew?

a	*AB, BC*	b	*AB, WX*
c	*AB, XY*	d	*BC, XY*
e	*BC, YC*	f	*BC, YZ*
g	*CD, BC*	h	*CD, YZ*
i	*CD, XB*		

2   Two straight roads *EF* and *PQ* and the footpath *UV* are all crossed by the telephone line *LM*.

Do these pairs of lines intersect, are they parallel or are they skew?

a	*EF, PQ*	b	*EF, LM*
c	*PQ, UV*	d	*PQ, LM*
e	*UV, EF*	f	*UV, LM*

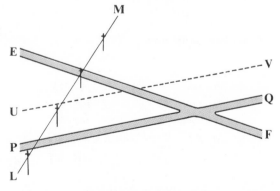

3

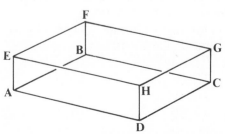

Write whether these pairs of edges of this cuboid intersect, are parallel or are skew.

a	*AB, DC*	b	*AD, EH*
c	*AB, FB*	d	*AB, HD*
e	*HD, CG*	f	*BF, FG*
g	*EF, FG*	h	*EF, DC*
i	*EF, GC*	j	*BC, HD*

155

Introducing three dimensions

4

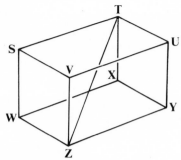

TZ is one of the diagonals of this cuboid.

Write whether these pairs of lines intersect, are parallel or are skew.

a   *WZ, XY*   b   *WZ, TZ*
c   *WZ, UY*   d   *YZ, TZ*
e   *XY, TZ*   f   *ST, ZY*
g   *ST, TZ*   h   *WX, TZ*
i   *SV, TZ*   j   *TZ, TU*

5   Write whether the following pairs of lines of this cube intersect, are parallel or are skew.

a   *OP, OR*   b   *OP, KL*
c   *OP, LM*   d   *QR, LK*
e   *QR, PK*   f   *OQ, OK*
g   *PN, PK*   h   *PK, QN*
i   *PN, OQ*   j   *PN, OK*

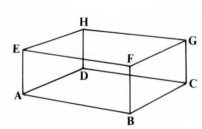

6

This diagram shows a cuboid.

Are the angles between the following pairs of lines 0° or 90°?

a   *AB, BC*   b   *AB, BF*
c   *BF, BC*   d   *AB, DC*
e   *AD, EH*   f   *AD, HG*
g   *EF, BC*   h   *AB, HG*
i   *HD, DC*   j   *FB, EH*

7   This cube has the diagonals *IN* and *IK* drawn on two of its faces.

Are the angles between these pairs of lines 0°, 45° or 90°?

a   *PL, LK*   b   *PL, OK*
c   *PL, ON*   d   *PL, MN*
e   *MN, IN*   f   *PO, IN*
g   *LI, KI*   h   *PM, KI*
i   *IJ, PO*   j   *OK, KI*

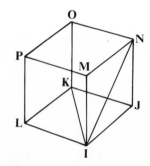

8

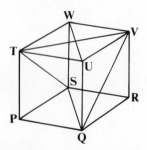

This diagram shows a cube with diagonals drawn on some of its faces.

Are the angles between the following pairs of lines 0°, 45° or 90°?

a   *UV, VW*   b   *UV, TV*
c   *TS, PS*   d   *UV, PS*
e   *TU, PS*   f   *TV, WU*
g   *TV, SQ*   h   *QV, TS*
i   *PS, QV*   j   *TS, VR*

Introducing three dimensions

9

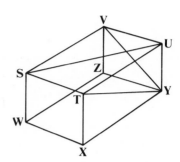

Name the angles between these pairs of lines.

(Do *not* give the *size* of the angle.)

a	*LM, BM*	b	*KN, BM*
c	*BC, BM*	d	*AD, BM*
e	*AB, BM*	f	*KL, BM*
g	*MC, BM*	h	*DN, BM*

10 Name the angles between these pairs of lines.

(Do *not* give the *size* of the angle.)

a	*WX, XY*	b	*TY, XY*
c	*VY, UY*	d	*ST, VY*
e	*SU, XY*	f	*SU, YZ*
g	*SU, WZ*	h	*TY, SV*
i	*UV, TX*	j	*TY, VY*

11

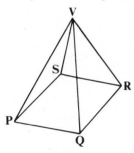

Name the angle between these pairs of lines.

a	*PV, PS*	b	*PQ, QV*
c	*SR, QR*	d	*PV, QV*
e	*PS, VQ*	f	*SR, VQ*
g	*PV, VR*	h	*VS, PQ*

12 This wedge has a rectangular base *KLMN* and two vertical isosceles triangles as sides.

Name the angle between these pairs of lines.

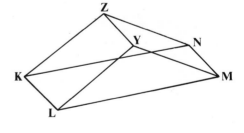

a	*KL, LM*	b	*KL, LY*
c	*ZK, NK*	d	*ZK, YM*
e	*ZN, LM*	f	*LY, NM*
g	*YZ, LM*	h	*YZ, KZ*

Write whether the angles between these pairs of lines are 0°, 90° or neither.

i	*KL, KN*	j	*KL, KZ*
k	*KL, ZY*	l	*LM, YM*
m	*YM, MN*	n	*YZ, ZN*
o	*KN, YM*	p	*KL, ZN*

13

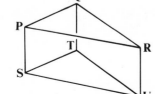

a Name two angles between the edges *PR* and *TU*.

b Name two angles between the edges *PQ* and *SU*.

c Name the two edges parallel to *PS*.

d Name the three edges perpendicular to *PQ*.

e Name the three edges skew with *PR*.

Introducing three dimensions

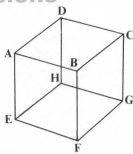

14 How many edges of this cube are
   a parallel to the edge *AD*
   b skew with the edge *AD*
   c perpendicular with the edge *AD*?

15

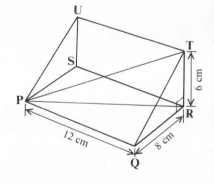

a Write without any calculation the size of the angles between these lines.
   (i) *AB, FB*   (ii) *AB, BC*
   (iii) *AB, BG*

b Use Pythagoras' theorem to calculate the length *BG*.

c Calculate the size of the angles between these lines.
   (i) *BG, BC*   (ii) *BG, BF*
   (iii) *BG, AB*   (iv) *BG, AG*

(NOTE: It is sometimes helpful to sketch a triangle separately, marking on it all the known angles and sides.)

16 a Calculate the length *QT* using Pythagoras' theorem.

   b Write, without any calculation, the size of the angles between these lines.
   (i) *SR, TR*   (ii) *QR, TR*
   (iii) *PR, TR*   (iv) *PQ, QR*
   (v) *PQ, QT*

   c Calculate the size of the angles between these lines.
   (i) *TQ, QR*   (ii) *PR, QR*
   (iii) *PT, PQ*   (iv) *PR, UT*

17

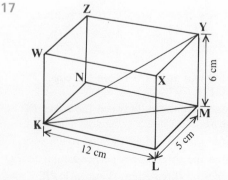

a Calculate the length *KM* using Pythagoras' theorem.

b Write, without any calculation, the size of the angles between these lines.
   (i) *LM, MY*   (ii) *KM, MY*
   (iii) *KM, NZ*   (iv) *KN, XY*
   (v) *KL, LM*

c Calculate the size of the angles between these lines.
   (i) *KM, KL*   (ii) *KM, LM*
   (iii) *KY, KM*   (iv) *KY, YM*
   (v) *KY, XL*

Introducing three dimensions

18 This pyramid has a rectangular base *ABCD* whose
centre *O* is 12 cm vertically below the vertex *V*.
a   What size are the angles between
(i) *AB*, *BC*   (ii) *AO*, *OV*?
b   Use Pythagoras' theorem to calculate
the lengths
(i) *AC*   (ii) *AO*   (iii) *AV*.
c   Calculate the size of the angles between
these lines.
(i) *AC*, *BC*   (ii) *AO*, *AV*
d   Sketch triangle *ABV* separately, where *M*
is the midpoint of *AB*. Join *VM* and find
(i)   angle *VMB*   (ii)   the angle between sides *AB* and *AV*.
e   Write, without any further calculation, the angle between *AV* and *DC*.

Part 2   Angles between lines and planes

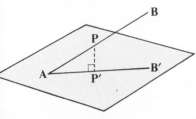

(i)   *When the line intersects the plane.*
The line *AB* intersects the plane at the
point *A*.
From any point *P*, a perpendicular is
dropped to *P′* on the plane. We say that
the *projection* of *AP* on the plane is *AP′*.
The angle between the line *AB* and the
plane is ∠*BAB′*.

Note that it is helpful to think of a light directly over the plane so that *AB′* is the
shadow of *AB* on the plane.

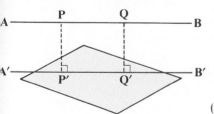

(ii)   *When the line is parallel to the plane.*
From any two points *P* and *Q* on line *AB*
perpendiculars are dropped to *P′* and *Q′*
on the plane. The projection *A′B′* of line
AB on the plane will pass through *P′* and *Q′*.
The angle between the line *AB* and the
plane is 0°.

(iii)   A line will *either* intersect a plane at a point
or be parallel to a plane
or lie in the plane.

1   You are standing at one end of a room, looking towards the other end.
For each of these pairs of lines and planes
does the line *intersect* the plane,
is it *parallel* to the plane
or does it *lie in* the plane?
a   *WX*, the floor *ABCD*
b   *XY*, the floor *ABCD*
c   *XB*, the floor *ABCD*
d   *YZ*, the floor *ABCD*
e   *YC*, the floor *ABCD*
f   *AB*, the floor *ABCD*
g   *YZ*, the wall *ABXW*
h   *BC*, the wall *ABXW*
i   *XB*, the wall *DCYZ*
j   *YC*, the wall *BCYX*

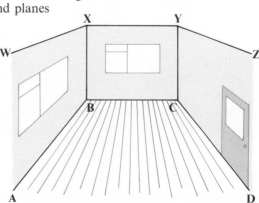

159

Introducing three dimensions

2   A horizontal radio aerial *AB* is
   supported on two vertical poles
   AY and *BZ* which are fixed to the
   ground by wires *AM* and *BN*.

   For each of these pairs of lines
   and planes
   does the line *intersect* the plane,
       is it *parallel* to the plane
   or does it *lie* in the plane?
   a   *AB*, the ground   b   *AY*, the ground   c   *AM*, the ground
   d   *YZ*, the ground   e   *AY*, the plane *ABZY*   f   *AB*, the plane *ABZY*

3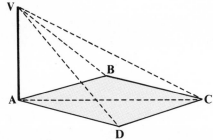

   A vertical pole *AV* stands in one
   corner of a horizontal rectangular plot
   of land *ABCD*.

   Which lines are the projections
   onto *ABCD* of
   a   *BV*   b   *CV*   c   *DV*?

4   A pyramid has a horizontal rectangular
   base *PQRS* with centre *X* directly below
   vertex *O*.

   Which lines are the projections onto the
   base of
   a   *OP*   b   *OQ*   c   *OR*
   d   *OS*?

   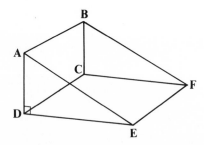

5   This wedge has a vertical face
   ABCD and a horizontal face *CDEF*.

   What is the projection of
   a   *AE* onto the face *CDEF*
   b   *BF* onto the face *CDEF*
   c   *AB* onto the face *CDEF*
   d   *AE* onto the face *ABCD*
   e   *BF* onto the face *ABCD*
   f   *EF* onto the face *ABCD*?

6   A ladder *PQ* leans against the corner of
   two vertical walls which meet at right
   angles.

   What is the projection of *PQ* onto
   a   the ground
   b   the left-hand wall containing *P*,
       O and *X*
   c   the right-hand wall containing *P*,
       O and *Y*?

   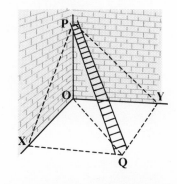

Introducing three dimensions

7 This open tray with a base and three vertical sides contains a rod *FD*.

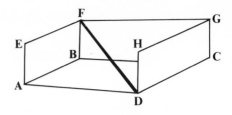

What is the projection of *FD* onto
a the plane *ABCD*
b the plane *ABFE*
c the plane *BCGF*
d the plane *DHGC*?

8

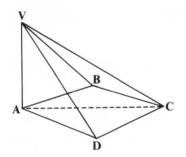

Say whether the angle between the line and the plane is 0° or 90°.

a *AB, EFGH*   b *AC, EFGH*
c *AD, EFGH*   d *AE, EFGH*
e *EF, ADHE*   f *FG, ADHE*
g *AD, DCGH*   h *AB, DCGH*
i *AB, BCGF*   j *AH, BCGF*
k *DH, BCGF*   l *DH, ABCD*

Write the projection of each point or line onto the given plane.
m point *A* onto *EFGH*   n point *C* onto *EFGH*   o point *A* onto *BCGF*
p point *H* onto *BCGF*   q point *H* onto *ABFE*   r point *C* onto *ABFE*
s line *AH* onto *EFGH*   t line *AD* onto *EFGH*   u line *CD* onto *EFGH*
v line *AC* onto *EFGH*   w line *EH* onto *BCGF*   x line *AC* onto *BCGF*

9 Name the angle between each line and plane.

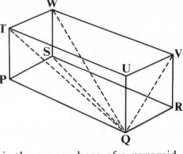

a *TQ, PQRS*   b *VQ, PQRS*
c *WQ, PQRS*   d *QV, RSWV*
e *QV, TUVW*   f *QT, TUVW*
g *SQ, RQUV*   h *WQ, RQUV*
i *SQ, PQUT*   j *WQ, PQUT*

10

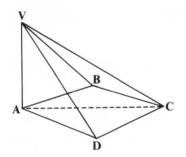

ABCD is the square base of a pyramid with a vertex *V* directly above corner *A*.

Name the angle between each edge and plane.
a *VB, ABCD*   b *VD, ABCD*
c *VC, ABCD*   d *VD, VAB*
e *VC, VAD*   f *VC, VAB*

11 A pyramid has a square base *WXYZ*, a vertex *V* directly above the centre *O* of the base, and *M* and *N* as midpoints of edges *YZ* and *WZ*.

Name the angle between each line and plane.
a *WV, WXYZ*   b *ZV, WXYZ*
c *NV, WXYZ*   d *WV, VXZ*
e *ZV, VWY*   f *YV, VXZ*
g *VM, WXYZ*   h *VM, VNO*

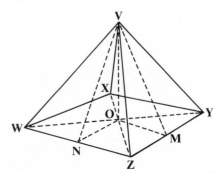

161

Introducing three dimensions

12 The cuboid shown has *M* as the midpoint
   of edge *GC*. Calculate
   a length *BD* using Pythagoras' theorem
   b the angle between *HB* and plane *ABCD*
   c the angle between *GB* and plane *ABCD*
   d the angle between *MB* and plane *ABCD*.

   (It may be helpful to draw separately each
   triangle used.)

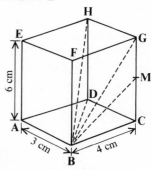

13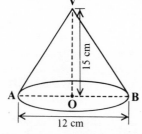

   A cone has a diameter *AB* 12 cm long
   and its vertex *V* 15 cm is directly above
   the centre of its base *O*.

   Calculate the angle between *VA* and the
   circular base.

14 Another cone of diameter *AB* 12 cm has its
   vertex *V* 15 cm directly above point *B*.

   If *O* is the centre of its base, calculate
   a the angle between *VA* and the circular
     base
   b the angle between *VO* and the circular
     base.

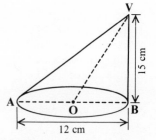

15 A pyramid has a rectangular base *PQRS* 8 cm by 6 cm. All its slant edges,
   PV, *QV*, *RV* and *SV*, are 10 cm long.

   M and *N* are midpoints of the sides *SR* and *PQ*. Calculate

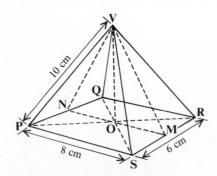

   a the lengths *PR* and *PO* using
     Pythagoras' theorem
   b the angle between *PV* and the
     base *PQRS*
   c the angle between *QV* and the
     base *PQRS*
   d the length *VM* (using
     triangle *VSM*)
   e the angle between *VM* and the
     base *PQRS*
   f the angle between *SV* and the
     plane *MNV*.

16 A cuboid has the dimensions shown.
   Calculate the angle between
   a *UX* and the base *WXYZ*
   b *UX* and the plane *UVZY*
   c *US* and the plane *UVZY*
   d *WY* and the plane *SVZW*
   e *XY* and the plane *SUYW*
   f *SV* and the plane *SUYW*.

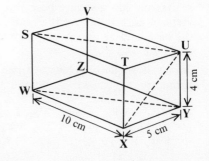

Introducing three dimensions

Part 3 Angles between two planes

(i) If two planes are parallel,
the angle between them is 0°.

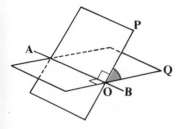

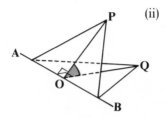

(ii) If two planes are not
parallel, they will have a
line of intersection AB.

The angle between the
planes is $\angle POQ$, where
both PO and QO are at
right angles to AB.

Note that it may be helpful to think of the line of
intersection AB as a hinge.

The angle POQ is the angle turned through by the
hinge as the planes close together.

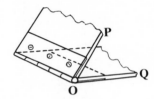

1

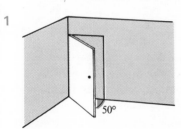

Two vertical walls meet at right angles and
a door in the corner opens through 50°.

What angle will the door make with the
other wall?

2 A rectangular sheet of glass leans against
a wall at an angle of 40° as shown.

What is the angle between the glass and
the ground?

3

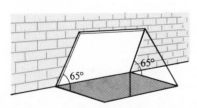

The hinge of a trapdoor is in the crack
between a vertical wall and the horizontal
floor.

If the door is propped open at 65° to the
floor, what angle does it make with the
wall?

4 Two wooden boards lean together so
that they are inclined at 50° and 30° to
the ground.

What is the angle between the two
boards?

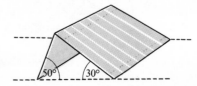

163

Introducing three dimensions

5 a

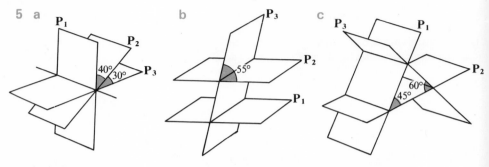

Each diagram shows three planes P_1, P_2 and P_3.

Find the acute angle between the planes P_1 and P_3 in each case.

6 A window is protected by two shutters which are shown partly opened at angles of 30° and 40° to the wall.

Calculate the angle α between the two shutters.

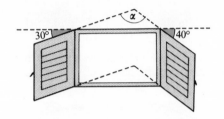

7

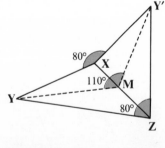

Two identical right-angled triangles PQR and $P'QR$ are positioned as shown standing on a horizontal surface.

Is the angle between the two triangles 120° or 100°?

8 Two planes in the shape of isosceles triangles XYZ and $XY'Z$ meet in the line XZ where M is the midpoint of XZ.

Is the angle between the two planes 80° or 110°?

9

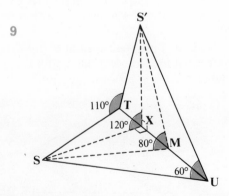

M is the midpoint of the side TU of the horizontal triangle STU.

X is the foot of the perpendicular from S to TU.

The triangle STU is now rotated onto triangle $S'TU$, producing the angles shown.

What is the angle between the two triangles (i.e. the angle of rotation)?

Introducing three dimensions

10

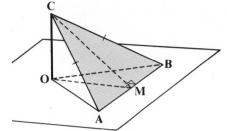

An isosceles triangle *ABC* with *M* the midpoint of *AB*, is held at an angle to the horizontal by a vertical rod *CO*.

Which *one* of these three angles is the angle between the triangle and the horizontal?

a ∠*CAO* b ∠*CMO*
c ∠*CBO*

11 *M* is the midpoint of the side *AB* of the triangle *ABC* which is *not* isosceles. *X* is the foot of the perpendicular from *C* to *AB*.

The triangle is held at an angle to the horizontal plane by a vertical rod *CO*.

Which *one* of these four angles is the angle between the triangle and the horizontal?

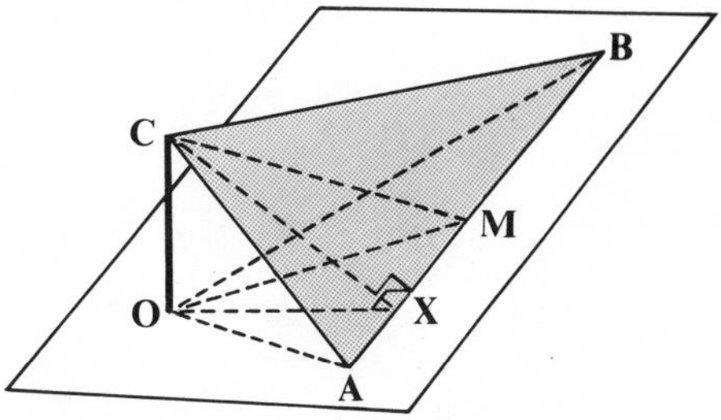

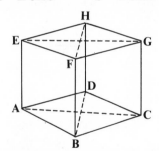

a ∠*CAO* b ∠*CXO* c ∠*CMO* d ∠*CBO*

12

The diagram shows a cube with base *ABCD* and top *EFGH*.

Write whether the angles between these pairs of planes are 0°, 90° or 45°.

a *ABFE, BCGF* b *ADHE, DCGH*
c *ABCD, EFGH* d *BCGF, ADHE*
e *ACGE, BCGF* f *ACGE, DCGH*
g *ACGE, ABCD* h *BFHD, ADHE*
i *BFHD, EFGH* j *ACGE, BFHD*

13 A wedge with a square base *ABYX* has an isosceles right-angled triangle *ABC* as a cross-section.

Write whether the angles between the following pairs of planes are 0°, 90° or 45°.

a *ABYX, YZCB* b *ABYX, ACZX*
c *ABC, XYZ* d *ABC, ABYX*
e *XBC, ABYX* f *AXZC, ZCBY*
g *XYZ, ZCBY* h *XBC, ABC*
i *XBC, XYZ* j *ACZX, ABC*

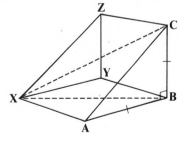

14

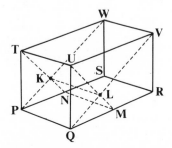

Name the angle between each pair of planes.

a *PQVW, PQRS*
b *PQVW, TUVW*
c *TUMN, TUQP*
d *TUMN, PQRS*
e *WVRS, PQRS*
f *TUMN, PQVW*

Introducing three dimensions

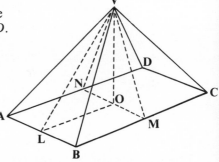

15   A pyramid has its vertex V directly above the centre O of its rectangular base $ABCD$.

L, M, N are the midpoints of the edges shown.

Name the angle between each pair of planes.
   a VAB, $ABCD$ b VBC, $ABCD$
   c VAD, $ABCD$ d VLO, VMO
   e VAB, VMN f VBC, VAD

16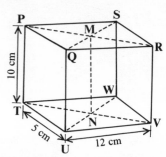

The cuboid shown has points M and N as the midpoints of edges AW and DZ.

Calculate the angles between these planes.
   a $WXYZ$, $MXYN$ b $WXYZ$, $AXYD$

Write, without any further use of trigonometry, the angle between these planes.
   c $MXYN$, $AXYD$ d $AXYD$, $BXYC$
   e $MXYN$, $BXYC$

17   Points M and N are the midpoints of the top and bottom faces of the cuboid, whose height is 10 cm, length 12 cm and width 5 cm.
   a   Sketch the top view of the cuboid showing the position M on face $PQRS$. What kind of triangle is $\triangle PMQ$?
   b   Calculate the angle between planes $PRVT$ and $PQUT$.
   c   Write the angle between planes $QSWU$ and $PQUT$.
   d   Name the line in which the diagonal planes $PRVT$ and $QSWU$ meet.
   e   Find the angle between planes $PRVT$ and $QSWU$.

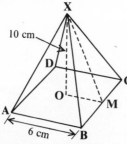

18   A square-based pyramid has its vertex X directly above the midpoint O of its base.

If the base has side 6 cm and the height is 10 cm, calculate the angle between the slanting face XBC and the base $ABCD$.

19   A cuboid has a square base of side 5 cm and midpoint X. Its height is 14 cm.
   a   Calculate the lengths FH and FX to two significant figures.
   b   Calculate the angle between the slanting plane GIJ and the base $FGHI$.

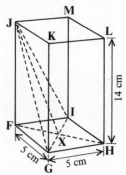

Introducing three dimensions

20 A pyramid has a rectangular base 8 cm by 6 cm and a height *PX* of 10 cm, where the vertex *X* is vertically above corner *P*.

Calculate the angle between
a   the face *XSR* and the base *PQRS*
b   the face *XQR* and the base *PQRS*.

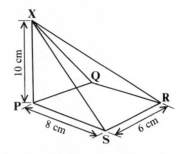

21

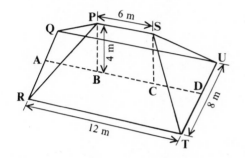

A roof of a house has the shape shown, where the ridge *PS* is 6 m long and the base *QRTU* is a rectangle 12 m by 8 m. *PS* is 4 m vertically above the base, so that *PB = SC = 4* m.
a   Copy the diagram and add further lines as required.

Calculate the angles between these planes.
b   *STU, QRTU*
c   *PRTS, QRTU*
d   *PRTS, PQUS*
e   *STU, PQR*

Cuboids, wedges and pyramids

Part 1

1
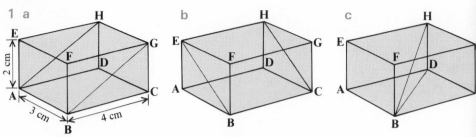

a   b   c

This cuboid stands 2 cm high on a rectangular base 3 cm by 4 cm.

Find   **a** the angle between planes *ABGH* and *ABCD*
      the angle between planes *ABGH* and *ABFE*

      b the angle between planes *BCHE* and *ABCD*
      the angle between planes *BCHE* and *BCGF*

      c the length *BD* using Pythagoras' theorem
      the angle between *BH* and the plane *ABCD*.

2   *O* is the midpoint of the base *KLMN* of
this cuboid. Calculate
   a   the lengths *KM* and *OM*
   b   the angle between the line *OY* and the
      plane *KLMN*
   c   the angle between the line *KY* and
      the plane *KLMN*.

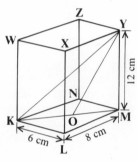

3
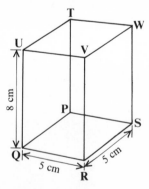

A cuboid has a square base of side 5 cm
and a height of 8 cm.

Draw diagrams to help you answer these
problems.

Write, without any calculation, the angle
between these planes.
   a   *SQUW, PQRS*   b   *SQUW, UVRQ*
   c   *SQUW, UTPQ*   d   *SQUW, PRVT*
Calculate the angles between these planes.
   e   *QRWT, PQRS*   f   *RSTU, PQRS*

4   A cuboid has a base 8 cm by 9 cm and a
height of 5 cm.

Calculate the angles between these planes.
   a   *AFGD, ABCD*
   b   *BEHC, ABCD*
   c   *AFGD, BEHC*

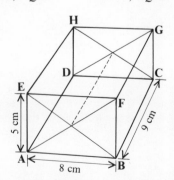

Cuboids, wedges and pyramids

5 *M* and *N* are the midpoints of the edges
FG and *BC* of this cuboid.

Write, without any calculation, the angle
between these planes
a   *ANME, ABCD*   b   *ACGE, ABCD*

Calculate the angle between these planes.
c   *ANME, ABFE*   d   *ACGE, ABFE*
e   *ANME, ACGE*

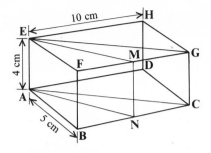

6

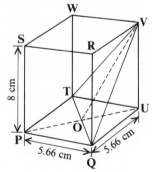

A cube has edges of 7.07 cm and *M*
is the midpoint of edge *UY*. Find
a   the length *SU* using Pythagoras'
    theorem
b   the angle between *SM* and
    plane *STUV*
c   the angle between *SY* and
    plane *STUV*
d   the angle between *SY* and *SM*.

7 A cuboid has a height of 8 cm
and a square base of side 5.66 cm
and centre *O*.
a   Use Pythagoras' theorem to
    calculate the lengths *PU* and *OU*.
b   Calculate the angle between
    the triangular plane *TQV* and
    the base *PQUT*.

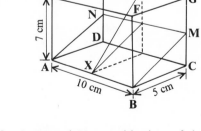

8

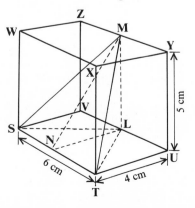

M, *N* and *X* are the midpoints of
the edges of the cuboid shown.

Calculate the angle between
a   the planes *ABMN* and *ABCD*
b   the line *XY* and the plane *ABCD*
c   the line *XY* and the plane *ABMN*.

9 *L*, *M* and *N* are midpoints of three
edges of this cuboid.
Calculate
a   the angle between the triangular
    plane *STM* and the base *STUV*
b   the length *LT* using triangle *LTU*
c   the angle between the line *MT*
    and the base plane *STUV*.

Cuboids, wedges and pyramids

10 This prism has a semicircular cross-section of diameter 6 cm, with L, M and N the midpoints of three edges. Calculate
   a the lengths LN and LS in triangle SLN
   b the angle between the triangular plane STM and the base plane
   c the angle between the line MS and the base plane.

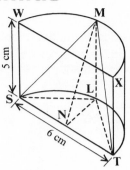

11
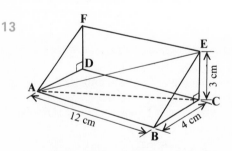

This wedge has a right-angled triangle as a cross-section. Calculate
   a the angle between the sloping face $GHIJ$ and the base plane $KHIL$
   b the length of the slanting edge IJ
   c the area of the sloping face $GHIJ$.

12 This wedge has an isosceles triangle as a cross-section with $AC = BC = 12$ cm.

   If the edge AB is 10 cm long with a midpoint M, calculate
   a the angle between the plane $BYZC$ and the base $ABYX$
   b the angle between the plane $BYZC$ and the vertical plane $MNZC$
   c the angle between the two sloping planes $BYZC$ and $AXZC$.

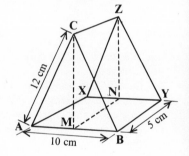

13
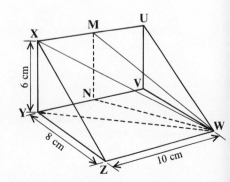

A wedge has a cross-section in the shape of a right-angled triangle BEC. Find
   a the length BE using triangle BEC
   b the length AE using triangle ABE
   c the angle between the sloping face $ABEF$ and the base plane $ABCD$
   d the angle between the line AE and the base plane $ABCD$.

14 Triangle XYZ is right-angled at Y and forms the cross-section of a wedge. M and N are the midpoints of the edges XU and YV. Calculate
   a the length XZ using triangle XYZ
   b the length XW using triangle WXZ
   c the angle between the line XW and the base $VYZW$
   d the length MW using triangle WUM
   e the angle between the line MW and the base $VYZW$.

Cuboids, wedges and pyramids

5   This wedge is made from two planes equally inclined to the horizontal base
so that triangle *PQR* is isosceles with *PR* = *QR* = 8 cm. Calculate
   a   the height *RN* of the wedge
   b   the area of triangle *PQR* and the
       volume of the wedge, both to three
       significant figures
   c   the angle between the sloping
       face *PRZX* and the base
       plane *PQYX*
   d   the angle between the sloping
       face *PRZX* and the vertical
       plane *NRZM*
   e   the angle between the two sloping
       faces *PRZX* and *QRZY*.

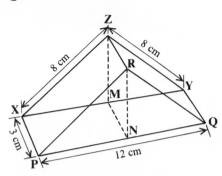

6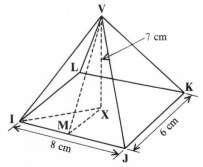

The base of this wedge is an isosceles
triangle *ABC* in which *AB* = *AC* = 10 cm
and *BC* = 12 cm. *M* is the midpoint of the
edge *BC*.
   a   Write, without any calculation the size
       of angle *AMB*.
Calculate
   b   the angle *BAM*
   c   the angle of the wedge between the
       planes *ABQP* and *ACRP*
   d   the length *AM* using triangle *BAM*
   e   the angle between the triangular
       plane *PBC* and the base *ABC*.

7   A wedge is made by cutting a cube in half so that the two square faces *ABCD*
and *ABFE* have edges 5 cm long.
   a   Calculate the angle between the sloping
       face *EFCD* and the base *ABCD*.

The wedge is then cut again along the
plane *AFC* to form a triangular-based
pyramid with *O* the midpoint of *AC*.
   b   Using triangle *BDC*, calculate the
       lengths *DB* and *OB*.
   c   Calculate the angle between the
       triangular plane *AFC* and the base
       plane *ABC*.

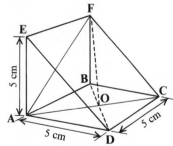

8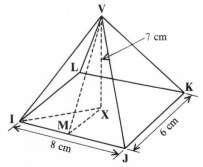

A pyramid has a rectangular base *IJKL*
8 cm by 6 cm and a vertex *V* 7 cm above
the centre of the base *X*.
M is the midpoint of the edge *IJ*.
   a   Use triangle *MXV* to calculate the
       angle between the sloping face *IJV*
       and the base.
   b   Use triangle *IXM* to calculate the
       length *IX*.
   c   Calculate the angle between the
       slanting edge *IV* and the base.

Cuboids, wedges and pyramids

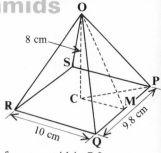

19 C is the centre of the rectangular base $PQRS$ of a pyramid of height 8 cm and M is the midpoint of the edge PQ. Calculate
 a the angle between the sloping face OPQ and the base $PQRS$
 b the length CP
 c the angle between the edge OP and the base.

20

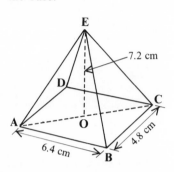

The vertex E of a pyramid is 7.2 cm directly above the centre O of its rectangular base $ABCD$.
 a Use triangle ABC to calculate the length AC.
 b Write the length AO.
 c Calculate the angle between the edge AE and the base.
 d What is the angle between AE and EO?
 e Write the angle between the two slanting edges AE and CE.

21 A pyramid has a height UV of 6 cm and a square base $WXYZ$ of side 7 cm.
 a Use triangle WYZ to calculate the lengths WY and UY.
 b Use triangle UVY to calculate the angle between the edge VY and the vertical UV.
 c Write the size of the angle between the two edges WV and YV.

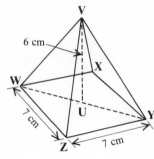

22

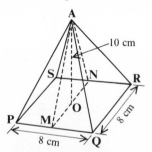

A square $PQRS$ of side 8 cm is the base of a pyramid which has a height OA of 10 cm.
 a Use triangle AMO to calculate the angle between the plane APQ and the horizontal base $PQRS$.
 b Calculate the angle between the plane APQ and the vertical line AO.
 c Calculate the angle between the two planes APQ and ASR.

23 A square $ABCD$ of side 12 cm is the base of a pyramid which has its vertex Y directly above the centre X of the square.
 The four slanting edges AY, BY, CY and DY are all 10 cm long. M and N are the midpoints of the sides AB and CD.
 a Use triangle YND to calculate the length YN.
 b Use triangle YNX to calculate the angle between the plane YCD and the base $ABCD$.
 c Calculate the angle between the plane YCD and the vertical.
 d Calculate the angle between the two planes YAB and YCD.

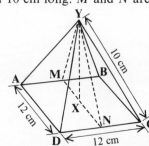

Cuboids, wedges and pyramids

Part 2   Applied problems

Give the answers to three significant figures where necessary.

1

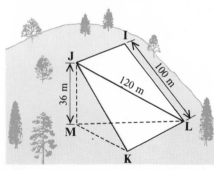

A garden shed has the shape of a cuboid with a base 3 metres by 4 metres and a height of 2 metres. *AG* is the longest wooden rod which can be stored in the shed.

a Use $\triangle ABC$ to calculate the length *AC*.

b Use $\triangle ACG$ to calculate the length of this longest rod *AG*.

c Calculate the angle which the rod *AG* makes with the ground.

2   A gift is packaged in a cardboard box which is divided into two parts by a sloping rectangular piece of cardboard *PQVW*.

Use the dimensions shown to calculate

a the length of the slant *QV*

b the area of the sloping rectangular piece of card

c the angle which this sloping piece makes with the base of the box *RSWV*.

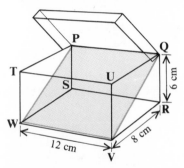

3

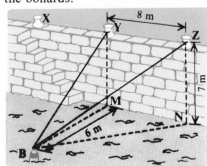

An artificial ski-slope *IJKL* runs downhill through a distance *IL* of 100 metres as it drops vertically *JM* 36 metres.

a Calculate the inclination of the slope to the horizontal.

b A skier goes straight from *J* to *L* which is a distance of 120 metres. Calculate the inclination of his path to the horizontal.

4   Bollards *X*, *Y* and *Z* on the edge of a harbour wall are 8 metres apart. The surface of the sea is 7 metres below the bollards.

A buoy *B* is fixed 6 metres out from the wall, and is tied to the bollards *Y* and *Z* by ropes *BY* and *BZ*. Calculate

a the length of the rope *BY*

b the distance *BN*

c the length of the rope *BZ*

d the inclination of the rope *BY* to the surface of the water

e the inclination of the rope *BZ* to the surface of the water.

173

Cuboids, wedges and pyramids

5 A primary school playground has a
   rectangular piece of tarmac *ABCD*
   6 m by 6.7 m with a telegraph pole
   5.4 m high in one corner.
   a Find the length of the diagonal
      AC, to two significant figures.
   b A child sits at *B* and looks at
      the top of the pole. What is the
      angle of elevation of *T* from *B*?
   c Calculate the angle of elevation
      of *T* from *C*.

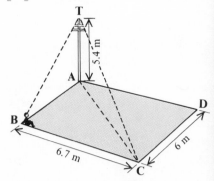

6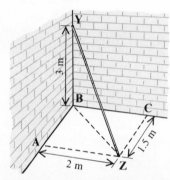

   A rod *YZ* has its lower end *Z* on a
   floor and its upper end *Y* rests in the
   crack between two vertical walls.

   Z is 2 metres from one wall and
   1.5 metres from the other, as shown.
   Y is 3 metres above the floor.
   a Use $\triangle ABZ$ to calculate the
      length *BZ*.
   b Calculate the length of the rod *YZ*.
   c Calculate the angle of inclination of
      the rod to the horizontal.

7 A television mast *OT* is 12 metres tall and is held vertical by four equal wires
   connected to the midpoint *M* of the mast and also to the ground at the four
   corners of a square *PQRS*.

   If the square has sides 7.07 metres long,
   calculate
   a the length of the diagonal *PR* using $\triangle PRS$
   b the distance *OP*
   c the length of the wire *PM*
   d the angle between the wire *PM* and
      the ground
   e the angle between the wire *PM* and
      the mast
   f the angle between the two wires *PM*
      and *MR*.

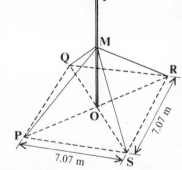

8 A man stands at a point *P* which is 10 metres due south of a church tower *CT*.
   The angle of elevation of the top of the tower *T* from *P* is 52°.

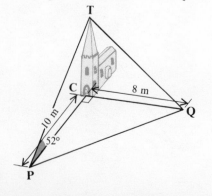

   He then walks directly from *P* to a
   point *Q* which is 8 metres due east of
   the tower. Calculate
   a the height *CT* of the tower
      using $\triangle PTC$
   b the angle of elevation of *T* from *Q*
   c the distance *PQ* which the man
      walks
   d the bearing on which he walks
      from *P* to *Q*, to the nearest whole
      degree.

Cuboids, wedges and pyramids

9   A hole *PQRS* in the floor is fitted with a rectangular trapdoor *PQ'R'S* which is shown held vertically open by a rod *Q'R*. Calculate
   a   the length of the diagonal *PR* using △*PQR*
   b   the length of the rod *Q'R*
   c   the angle which the rod *Q'R* makes with the horizontal.

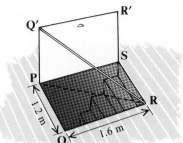

10

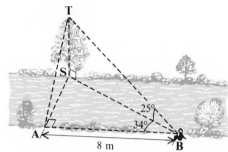

A tree *TS* stands on a river bank directly opposite a point *A*. Point *B* is 8 m further along the same bank.

A man at *B* measures angle *ABS* as 34° and the angle of elevation of *T* as 25°. Calculate
   a   the width of the river *AS*
   b   the distance *SB*
   c   the height of the tree *TS*.

11   A map shows a village *U* 4 km due south of a hilltop *T* and a second village *V* 5 km due east of *T*.

U and V are on the same contour line and *T'* is the point directly below *T* on the same level as *U* and *V*.

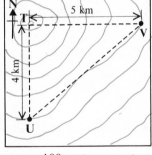

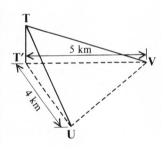

   a   If the contours on the map are 100 metres apart, what is the height *TT'*
       (i) in metres   (ii) in kilometres?
Calculate
   b   the angle of elevation of *T* from *U*   c   the angle of elevation of *T* from *V*
   d   the shortest distance between the two villages.
   e   On what bearing is *V* from *U*, to the nearest whole degree?

12   *HIJK* is a rectangular ramp used to load goods and vehicles from a dockside onto a ship. It is 3 m wide and 4 m long, rising at an angle of 29° to the horizontal.

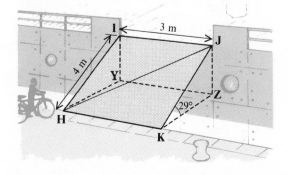

   a   Use △*JKZ* to calculate the vertical height *JZ* which the ramp rises.
   b   A cyclist pushes his bicycle onto the ship along the line *HJ*. Use △*HIJ* to calculate the distance *HJ* which he walks up the ramp.
   c   Calculate the angle of inclination of *HJ* to the horizontal.

Cuboids, wedges and pyramids

13 A horizontal square *ABCD* of side 9.9 cm is folded along its diagonal *BD* so that
the corner *A* rotates about *BD* to reach *A'* where the triangle *A'BD* is vertical.

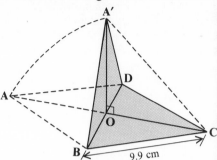

a Write, without any calculation, the
angle between the two triangular
planes *A'BD* and *CBD*.

b Use △*ABC* to calculate the lengths
of *AC* and *OC*.

c Calculate the shortest distance
from *A'* to *C*.

d Take π as $\frac{22}{7}$ and calculate the
distance travelled by *A* as it rotates
to *A'*.

14 A gardener makes a lean-to by placing a rectangular board 2 m by 3 m
against a wall at 57° to the ground.

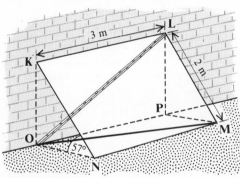

a Use △*OKN* to calculate
(i) how high *K* is above *O*
(ii) how far *N* is from *O*.

b A pole will just fit on the
ground between *O* and *M*.
Calculate its length.

c The gardener's bamboo canes
will just reach from *L* to *O*.
Find their length.

d Calculate the angle at which
these canes are inclined to the
horizontal.

15 An observer *O* sees an aeroplane *A* due north of him at an angle of elevation
of 32°. *B* is the point on the ground vertically below *A* and *OB* is 6 km.

The aeroplane is flying due east at a constant height and, one minute later, the
observer sees it at point *Y*. *Z* is the point on the ground vertically below *Y* and
the bearing of *Z* from *O* is 060°.

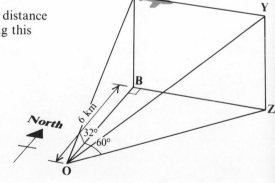

a Use △*OAB* to calculate the height
of the plane above *B*.

b Use △*OBZ* to calculate the distance
travelled by the plane during this
minute of observation.

c At what speed (in km/h) is
the plane flying?

d Calculate the distance *OZ*.

e Calculate the angle of
elevation of *Y* from *O*.

Surveying

Part 1   Building surveys

The walls of buildings are usually built so that they meet in corners at right angles. By measuring the lengths of the walls, a plan can be made.

Use the given scales to draw an accurate plan of each of the rooms or buildings shown here as rough sketches.

A ruler, a protractor or set square and a sharp pencil will be required.

1   A bungalow

Scale 1 cm = 1 m

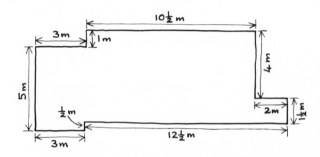

2   A living room of a house

Scale 1 cm = $\frac{1}{2}$ m

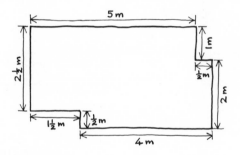

3   Two semi-detached houses

Scale 1 cm = 1 m

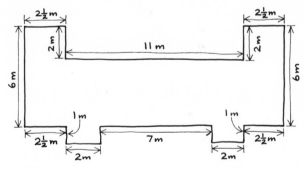

4   A factory

Scale 1 cm = 10 m

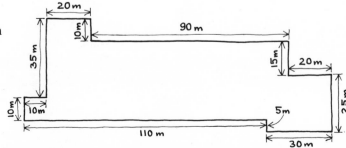

Surveying

5 A warehouse
Scale 1 cm = 10 m

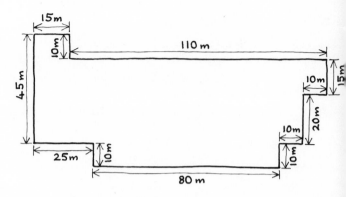

6 By dividing each of these five plans into rectangles, find the total area of each plan.

Part 2 Radial surveys

A radial survey is made by taking a point P from which all the points to be surveyed can be seen.

The direction of each point from P is fixed and its distance from P is measured.
In this exercise, the directions are given as bearings in degrees and the distances are given in metres.

Use the given scales to draw an accurate plan for each of these rough sketches.

A ruler, a protractor and a sharp pencil will be required.

1 A farmer's field
Scale 1 cm = 10 m

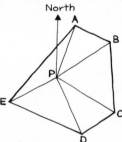

	Distance	Bearing
A from P	65 m	015°
B from P	77 m	050°
C from P	82 m	115°
D from P	75 m	140°
E from P	52 m	235°

Use a ruler to measure the lengths of the edges of the field and so find its perimeter.

2 Trees in a park
Scale 1 cm = 10 m

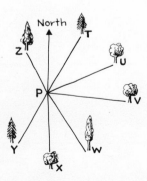

	Distance	Bearing
T from P	65 m	030°
U from P	75 m	065°
V from P	82 m	095°
W from P	80 m	145°
X from P	61 m	175°
Y from P	65 m	210°
Z from P	30 m	340°

Starting at T, what is the shortest distance you have to walk to visit all the other trees before returning to T?

Surveying

3 A children's playground
   Scale 1 cm = 10 m

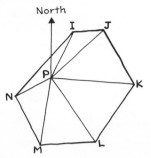

	Distance	Bearing
I from P	65 m	020°
J from P	80 m	035°
K from P	85 m	090°
L from P	72 m	135°
M from P	56 m	185°
N from P	25 m	245°

Take measurements with a ruler from the plan to find the perimeter of the playground.

4 A sports field
   Scale 1 cm = 10 m

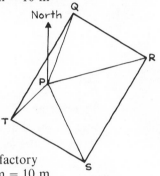

	Distance	Bearing
Q from P	61 m	020°
R from P	84 m	075°
S from P	70 m	155°
T from P	42 m	228°

Measure the width and length of the sports field and then calculate its area.

5 Part of a factory
   Scale 1 cm = 10 m

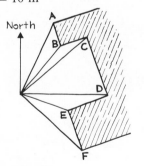

	Distance	Bearing
A from P	69 m	028°
B from P	60 m	040°
C from P	83 m	049°
D from P	82 m	090°
E from P	47 m	107°
F from P	73 m	129°

What is the distance from corner A to corner F around the walls of the factory?

Part 3   Triangulation

A triangle can be drawn when the lengths of its three sides are known.

Use the given scales to draw an accurate plan from each of these rough sketches.

A ruler, a sharp pencil and a pair of compasses will be required.

1 Use a scale of 1 cm = 10 m.

A straight path runs between two trees A and C.

Use a ruler to find the shortest distance from tree B to this path.

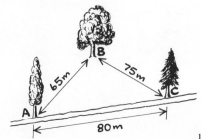

Surveying

2

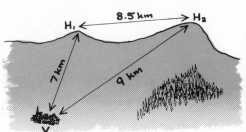

Use a scale of 1 cm = 10 m.

Two electricity pylons P and Q stand in the same field as a barn B.

Use a ruler to find the shortest distance from the barn B to the line joining P and Q.

3 Use a scale of 1 cm = 1 km.

A village V can be seen from two hill tops H_1 and H_2.

If a man walks direct from V to H_2, what is the closest he comes to hilltop H_1?

4

Use a scale of 1 cm = 1 km.

Two churches C and D can both be seen from the hilltops I and J.

What is the shortest distance between I and D?

5 Use a scale of 1 cm = 10 m.

A straight track AC runs diagonally across a field $ABCD$.

a What is the shortest distance from B to the track?

b What is the shortest distance between B and D?

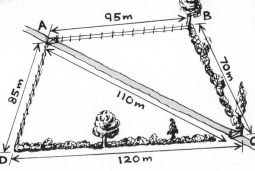

6

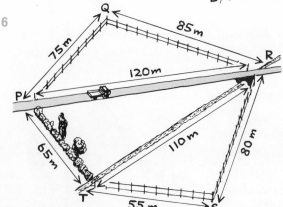

Use a scale of 1 cm = 10 m.

A straight road PR runs through three plots of land bounded by fences, a hedge PT and a water channel RT.

What is the shortest distance
a from Q to the road
b from S to the waterchannel
c between P and S?

7

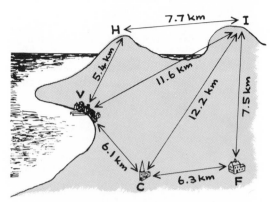

Use a scale of 1 cm = 1 km.

Two hills *H* and *I* rise behind a coastal village *V*.

The church *C* and farm *F* are inland.

a How far is the farm from the village?

b How far is the church from hill *H*?

c If a man walks direct from the farm to the village, what is the closest he comes to the church?

8 Tom Hartow grows vegetables on his allotment which has a triangular shape with sides of 16 m, 12 m and 8 m.

Use a scale of 1 cm for 2 metres to construct an accurate plan and use a ruler to help calculate the area of his allotment in m².

9 The roads and footpaths around a country church are shown here.

C church   R road bridge

F footbridge   S signpost

H house   T tree

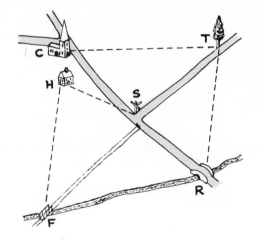

Use a scale of 1 cm for 10 metres and draw scale diagrams as described below.

a Given the distances *CT* = 120 m, *CS* = 90 m and *ST* = 100 m, construct the triangle *CST*.
Measure the shortest distance from *S* to *CT* and calculate the area of triangle *CST*.

b Given the distances *ST* = 100 m, *RT* = 90 m and *SR* = 65 m, construct the triangle *STR*.
Measure the shortest distance from *R* to *ST* and calculate the area of triangle *STR*.

c Given the distances *FR* = 118 m, *FS* = 105 m and *SR* = 65 m, construct the triangle *FRS*.
Measure the shortest distance from *S* to *FR* and calculate the area of triangle *FRS*.

d Given the distances *FH* = 112 m, *HS* = 60 m and *FS* = 105 m, construct the triangle *HSF*.
Measure the shortest distance from *S* to *HF* and calculate the area of triangle *HSF*.

Surveying

10 This sketch of several city streets shows five road junctions *A* to *E*.
Use a scale of 1 cm = 10 metres for the scale diagrams.

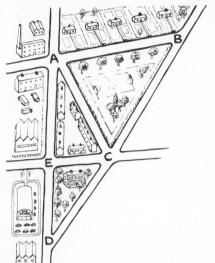

a Construct triangle *ABC* where
AB = 114 m, *BC* = 125 m and
CA = 98 m.
Measure the shortest distance from
C to *AB* and hence calculate the area
of the triangle.

b Construct triangle *ACE* where
AC = 98 m, *EC* = 54 m and
EA = 75 m.
Measure the shortest distance from
E to *AC* and hence calculate the area
of the triangle.

c Construct triangle *DEC* where
EC = 54 m, *CD* = 98 m and
DE = 60 m.
Choose one side as base, measure the
height and hence calculate the area of
the triangle.

Part 4   More triangulation

A triangle can also be drawn when the length of one side and the angles at either end
are known. The advantage of this method is that the surveyor need never visit the
third corner of the triangle.
Use a scale of 1 cm = 10 m to draw an accurate map for each of these.
A ruler, a protractor and a sharp pencil will be required.

1 Draw a base line *AB* 80 m long.

From *A*, a house *H* is 75° off the base line.
From *B*, the house is 30° off the base line.
Fix the position of the house *H*.

From *A*, a shop *S* is 40° off the base line.
From *B*, the shop is 80° off the base line.
On the same diagram, fix the position of the
shop *S*.

How far is
a the house from point *A*
b the shop from point *B*
c the house from the shop?

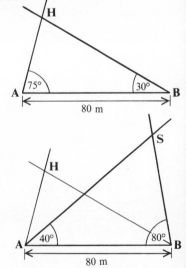

2 Draw a base line *AB* 70 m long.

From *A*, a shed *S* is 80° off the base line.
From *B*, the shed is 30° off the base line.

From *A*, a house *H* is 50° off the base line.
From *B*, the house is 45° off the base line.

From *A*, a garage *G* is 25° off the base line.
From *B*, the garage is 95° off the base line.
Fix the positions of *S*, *H* and *G*.

How far is
a the shed from point *A*   b the garage from point *B*
c the garage from the house   d the shed from the house?

Surveying

3   Draw a base line *AB* 60 m long.

From *A*, an oak tree *O* is 48° off the base line.
From *B*, the oak tree is 16° off the base line.

From *A*, a pine tree *P* is 25° off the base line.
From *B*, the pine tree is 65° off the base line.

From *A*, a sycamore tree *S* is 16° off the base line.
From *B*, the sycamore is 140° off the base line.

What is the distance between
a   the pine and the oak   b   the oak and the sycamore
c   the sycamore and the pine?

4   Draw a base line *AB* 55 m long.

From *A*, a footbridge *F* is 82° off the base line.
From *B*, the footbridge is 43° off the base line.

From *A*, a post office *P* is 22° off the base line.
From *B*, the post office is 149° off the base line.

From *A*, a church *C* is 64° *below* the base line.
From *B*, the church is 51° *below* the base line.

What is the distance between
a   the footbridge and the post office   b   the footbridge and the church
c   the post office and the church?

5   The four corners of a sports field can be seen from a base line *AB* which is 76 m long.

From *A*, the first corner is 22° *above* the base line.
From *B*, this corner is 60° *above* the base line.

From *A*, the second corner is 20° *below* the base line.
From *B*, this corner is 76° *below* the base line.

From *A*, the third corner is 103° *below* the base line.
From *B*, this corner is 24° *below* the base line.

From *A*, the fourth corner is 146° *above* the base line.
From *B*, this corner is 7° *above* the base line.

Join together the four corners of the sports field.
a   How long is the sports field in metres?   b   What is its width?
c   Calculate the area of the sports field in m².

6   A surveyor sets up a base line 80 m long, from which he can see a line of four telegraph poles.

1st pole: 30° above the base line from *A*
             70° above the base line from *B*

2nd pole: 24° above the base line from *A*
             42° above the base line from *B*

3rd pole: 13° above the base line from *A*
             12° above the base line from *B*

4th pole: 33° *below* the base line from *A*
             14° *below* the base line from *B*.

Draw the line of the telephone wires. What is the total length of the wires from the first to the fourth pole?

Surveying

7 Five lamp posts are erected along a road. From a base line AB 50 metres long, these readings are taken.

1st lamp post: 36° below the base line from A
                  71° below the base line from B

2nd lamp post: 16° below the base line from A
                  44° below the base line from B

3rd lamp post: 12° above the base line from A
                  22° above the base line from B

4th lamp post: 50° above the base line from A
                  27° above the base line from B

5th lamp post: 106° above the base line from A
                  22° above the base line from B

The lamp posts are connected by an underground cable which runs direct from one post to the next. Draw the cable on your map and find its length.

8 A farmer has three fields with corners at the farm F, a crossroads C, a group of trees T, a barn B and a phone box P. The distance BC is measured to be 96 m.

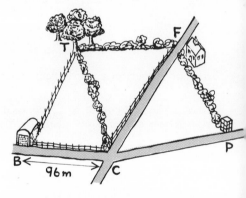

  a   Given that $\angle TBC = 85°$ and $\angle BCT = 48°$, construct triangle TBC, measure its height from T to BC and then calculate the area of field TBC.

  b   Given that $\angle TCF = 52°$ and $\angle CTF = 78°$, construct triangle TFC, measure its height from T to FC, the length of FC and then calculate the area of field TFC.

  c   Given that $\angle CFP = 59°$ and $\angle FCP = 38°$, construct triangle FCP and calculate its area.

9 Two hilltops H and I are 7.8 km apart. A third hilltop J is viewed firstly from H where angle JHI is 63° and secondly from I where angle HIJ is 74°.

Using a scale of 1 cm = 1 km, draw the line HI and construct the point J.

Use a ruler to help calculate the area of moorland enclosed by the triangle HIJ.

10 A triangular piece of derelict land in a city is enclosed by three straight roads which meet at points A, B and C.

The distance AB is 680 metres and the angles CAB and ABC are respectively 57° and 81°.

Use a scale of 1 cm = 100 m to draw the triangle ABC and hence calculate the area of this land.

Part 5   Offset surveys

A diagonal (or *survey line*) across the land to be surveyed is chosen and distances along it are measured from one end. Offsets are measured perpendicular to this survey line to fix the corners of the land or to fix any other points required.

A ruler, a protractor (or set square) and a sharp pencil will be required.

Surveying

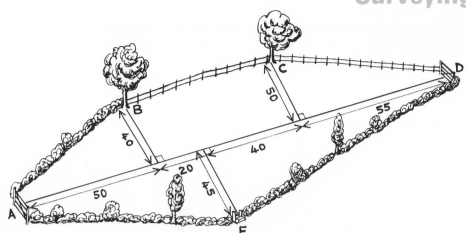

1   A field has corners *A*, *B*, *C*, *D* and *E*. The survey line *AD* is 165 metres long.

The measurements, called **offsets**, made at right angles to the survey line, fix the positions of the corners *B*, *C* and *E*.

As the measurements are taken in metres, they are recorded in a table shown below.

Note that distances along the survey line are recorded as being measured from the end *A*.

a   Copy and complete the table.

b   Draw a scale diagram of the field, using a scale of 1 cm = 10 metres.

c   Use a ruler to measure each of the five sides of the field and hence calculate its perimeter.

		To D	165	
C	50		---	
			70	--- E
B	---		50	
		From A	0	

2   A plot of land *VWXYZ* is to have a house built on it.

A survey is made using the survey line *VY* which is 70 m long.

Offsets are measured (in metres) as shown on the sketch.

a   Copy and complete the table.

b   Draw a scale diagram of the plot of land, using a scale of 1 cm = 10 metres.

c   Use a ruler to measure the sides of the plot and hence calculate its perimeter.

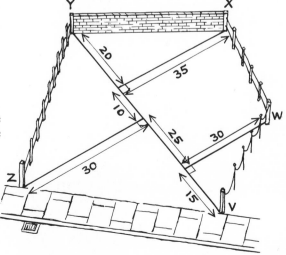

		To Y	70	
			---	35 X
Z	---		---	
			15	---W
		From V	0	

Surveying

3   Copy and complete each table from the measurements (in metres) given on the sketches.
Use a scale of 1 cm = 10 metres in each case and draw each shape accurately.
Use a ruler to measure the sides of each shape and calculate their perimeters.

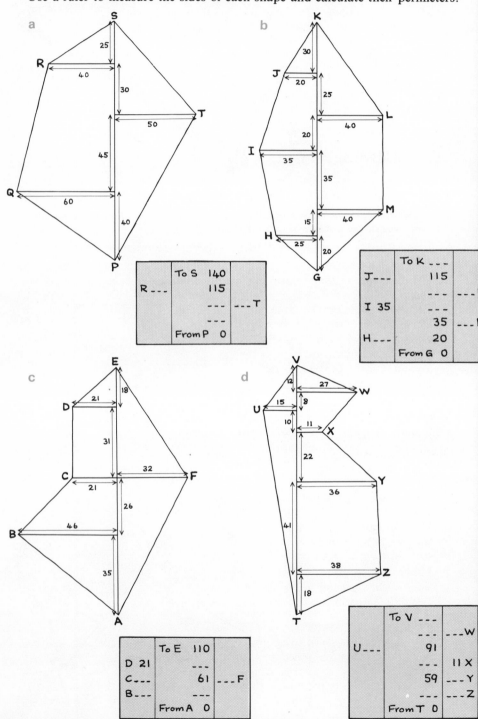

a

	To S	140	
R ---		115	
		---	--- T

	From P	0	

b

		To K	---	
J ---		115		
		---		--- L
I 35		---		
		35		--- M
H ---		20		
		From G	0	

c

	To E	110	
D 21		---	
C ---		61	--- F
B ---		---	
	From A	0	

d

		To V	---	
		---		--- W
U ---		91		
		---		11 X
		59		--- Y
		---		--- Z
		From T	0	

186

Surveying

4 Use a ruler to draw accurate diagrams to the given scale for each of these tables of measurements (all in metres).

By dividing each diagram into triangles and rectangles, calculate the area of each piece of land.

a
Scale 1 cm = 1 m

	To C	14	
B 3		10	
		8	6 D
		3	6 E
	From A	0	

b
Scale 1 cm = 1 m

	To L	16	
K 3		14	
		8	4 M
J 3		4	
	From I	0	

c
Scale 1 cm = 1 m

	To U	17	
Z 6		14	
		10	4 V
Y 6		5	
		2.5	4 W
	From X	0	

d
Scale 1 cm = 10 m

	To S	65	
R 34		45	
		40	32 T
Q 34	From P	0	

e
Scale 1 cm = 10 m

	To X	65	
		40	50 Y
W 42		25	
		10	30 Z
	From V	0	

f
Scale 1 cm = 10 m

	To C	100	
		80	20 D
B 34		45	
		30	20 E
		20	30 F
	From A	0	

5 A house has a garden with five sides.
A plan is made of the garden and this table gives the measurements in metres.

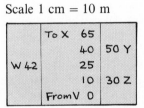

a Use a scale of 1 cm = 2 m to draw a map of the garden. Label its corners.
b Calculate the total area of the garden.
c Taking measurements from the map, find the perimeter of the garden.
d If the whole garden is turfed with grass costing 45 pence per m², what will be the total cost of the turf?

6 Planning permission is given for a caravan site to be set up on a plot of land. An offset survey is made of the plot in metres.

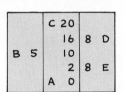

a Using a scale of 1 cm = 100 m, make a map of the site and find its area in square metres.
b If 1 hectare = 10 000 m², find the area of the site in hectares.
c 15% of the land is given over to services such as shops, roads and washrooms. Find this area in hectares.
d The other 85% of the land is occupied by caravans. If each caravan must have a space of 200 m², how many caravans can the site accommodate?
e If the site charges are £175 per caravan per year, what is the income in one year?

Surveying

7 An offset survey is made of a farmer's field with measurements taken in metres.
   a Using a scale of 1 cm = 10 m, make a map of
      the field and calculate its area.
   b Use the map to find the perimeter of the field.
   c The farmer drains the field by a ditch running
      round the perimeter. If, with the help of a machine,
      a ten-metre length of ditch takes 30 minutes to
      dig, how long will the whole perimeter take?
   d Along sides GA, AB and BC, new fencing is needed costing £1·25 per metre.
      Find the total cost of the fencing from G to C.

D 10	E 80	
	60	30 F
C 40	30	
	20	30 G
B 40	A 0	

8 A builder buys a piece of land on which he intends
   to build houses and shops. An offset survey (made
   in metres) is given here.
   a What is a suitable scale with which to draw a map
      of the plot?
   b A straight road is made 10 metres wide, with HL as
      the middle of the road. Draw the road on the map.
   c Estimate the length of the road and its area. If tarmac costs £1·65 per
      square metre, find the cost of tarmac for the road, to the nearest £100.
   d The land on one side of the road, bounded by HLMG, is divided equally into
      five plots for five shops. Find the area HLMG and the size of each plot.
   e The rest of the land HLKJI is for houses. Find this area. If each house
      needs 200 m², how many houses could be built?

	J 115	
I 40	95	75 K
	65	60 L
	25	60 M
H 40	20	
	G 0	

9 A small reservoir is built with vertical 12 m deep sides.
   Its surface has a shape given by an offset survey in
   metres as shown.
   a Choose a suitable scale and draw an accurate map
      of the surface of the reservoir, stating the scale used.
   b Calculate the area of the surface.
   c What is the capacity of the reservoir (i.e. how many
      cubic metres does it hold)?
   d Public safety requires the reservoir to be solidly fenced round the perimeter.
      Take measurements to find what length of fencing will be required.
   e If the fencing has to be 2 metres high, what is the area of the fencing?
   f The reservoir supplies a small factory which uses 50 m³ of water daily. For
      how many days, if necessary, could the reservoir keep the factory supplied?

	D 16	
C 4	13	5 E
B 6	6	
	2	7 F
	A 0	

10 In a city park the local council decides to plant flowers
    and shrubs along one side of a long straight path AB
    which is 110 metres long.
    To get some idea of the size of the operation, a
    groundsman makes an offset survey along the path
    taking measurements in metres.
    a Choose a suitable scale and draw an accurate map
       of the flower-bed.
    b Calculate the bed's area.
    c Half the bed is to be planted with flowers and the
       other half with shrubs. Eight flowering plants will
       take up 1 m² and one shrub will need 2 m². Find how many plants and
       shrubs are needed to fill the bed.

B 110	8 Z
100	14 Y
80	14 X
70	18 W
50	14 V
40	10 U
30	5 T
10	9 S
A 0	5 R

d On average, plants cost 12 pence each and shrubs £1·15 each. Find the total cost of plants and shrubs to the nearest £.

e This plan proves too expensive and 36% of the total must be cut back. What is the new amount to be spent on plants and shrubs (to the nearest £)?

Part 6   Contours

All heights on contour lines in this exercise are in metres.

1

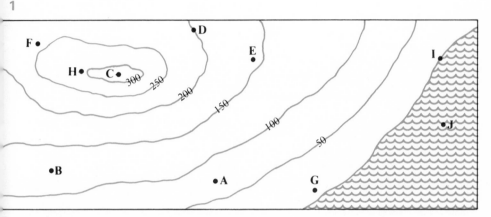

This map shows a hill near to the coast.

Ten points A to J are marked on it. Pair these points with the ten heights given here.

Example   Point A matches with **c** 70 m.

a 130 m	b 154 m	c 70 m	d 8 m	e 315 m
f 200 m	g 295 m	h −30 m	i 248 m	j 0 m

2

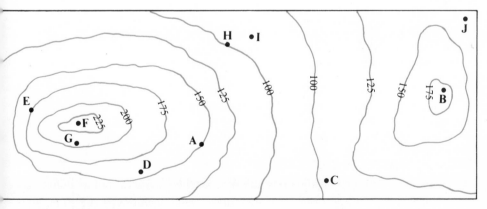

This map shows two hilltops.

Ten points are labelled A to J. Pair the points with these heights.

a 110 m	b 230 m	c 180 m	d 100 m	e 160 m
f 150 m	g 96 m	h 205 m	i 137 m	j 175 m

189

Surveying

3

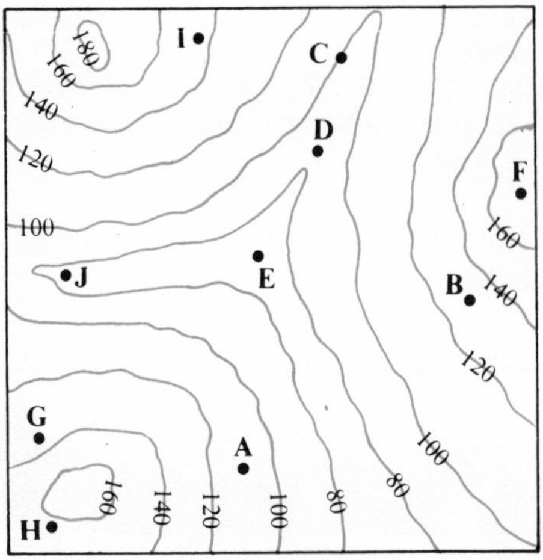

This map shows three hills around the head of a valley.

Write the approximate heights of the ten points A to J.

4

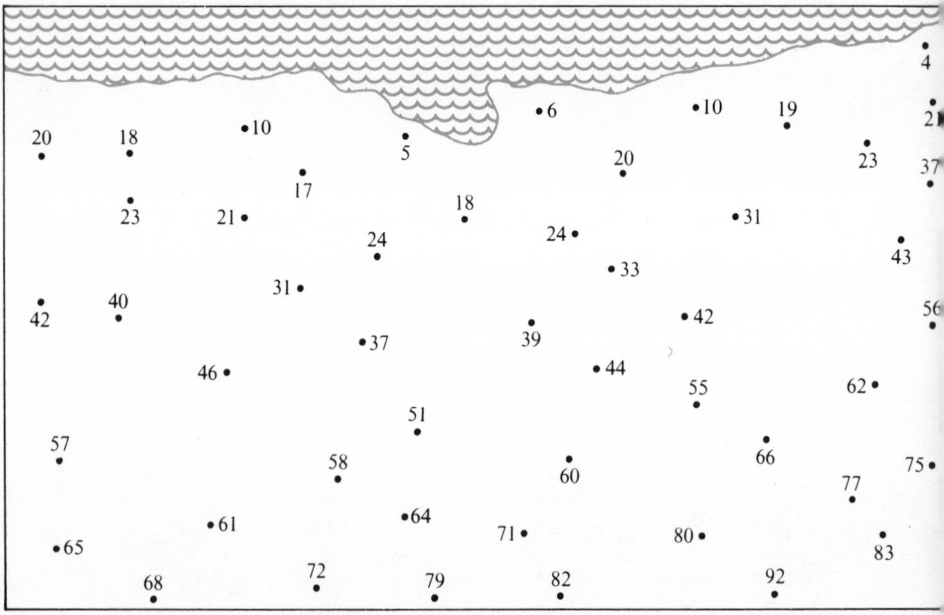

This map shows a coastline and the spot heights of several points inland.

Trace or copy it and draw on it the approximate positions of the 20 m, 40 m, 60 m and 80 m contour lines.

Surveying

5

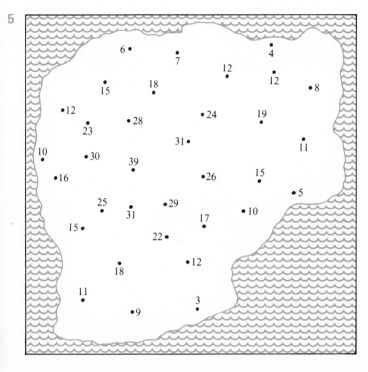

This is the map of an island on which the heights above sea-level are given for many points.

Trace or copy it and draw on it the approximate positions of the 10 m, 20 m and 30 m contour lines.

6

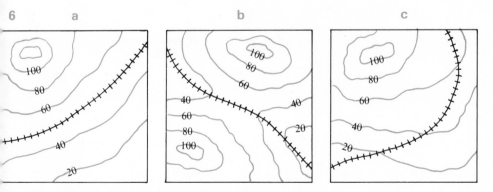

Each of these three maps shows a railway line in hilly country.

Match the maps **a**, **b**, **c** with these three descriptions.

X The line rises gradually as it passes a hill.

Y The line keeps the same height as it passes a hill.

Z The line crosses a pass between two hills.

Surveying

7

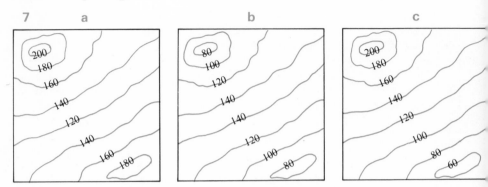

These three maps have contours of the same shape but of different heights.

Match the maps **a**, **b**, **c** with these three descriptions.

X Two hills with a valley between them.

Y A ridge with two depressions on either side.

Z A hill sloping down into a depression.

8

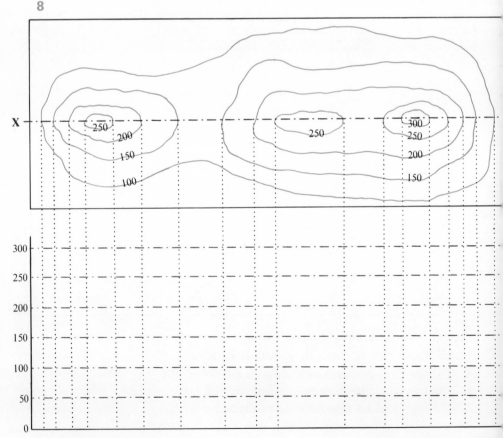

Trace or copy this diagram and, on *your* axes, draw a section of the map along the line XX'.

9

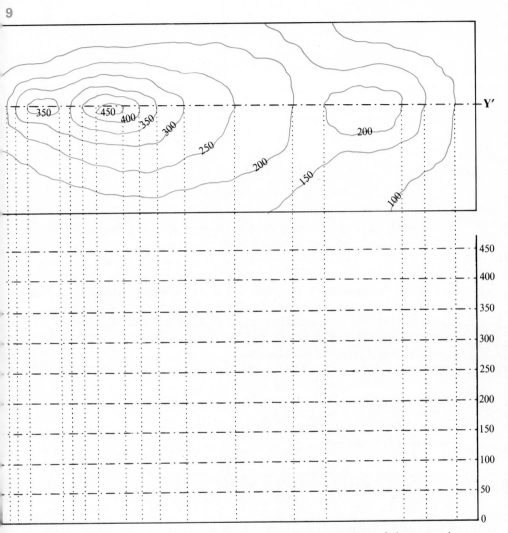

Trace or copy this diagram and, on *your* axes, draw a section of the map along the line *YY'*.

Surveying

10

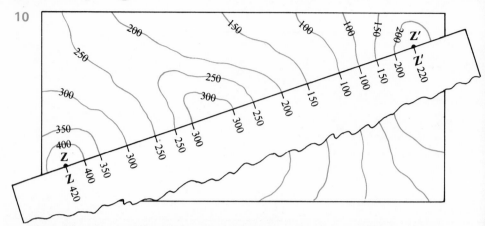

A section is to be drawn along the line between the two hilltops Z and Z' which are 420 metres and 220 metres high respectively.

This map shows the straight edge of a sheet of paper placed along the line ZZ'.

Mark Z and Z' on the edge of the paper and, where the edge crosses a contour line, mark the position on the paper and write the height. Repeat this along the edge for all contours from Z to Z'.

Draw the axes for your section on squared paper as shown in this sketch.

Place the edge of your paper on the ZZ' axis and plot a point for each contour line at the correct height. Finally, join the points smoothly to draw the section.

Imagine that you are standing on the hilltop Z'. Will you be able to see hilltop Z? Place a ruler across the section to find out.

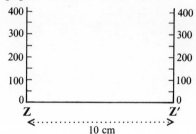

11

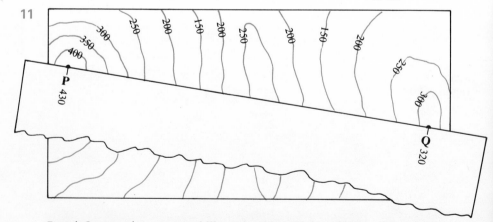

P and Q are points on two hills: P is 430 m high, and Q is 320 m high.

Place the edge of a sheet of paper along the line PQ as shown. Mark on it the contours which it crosses and their heights.

Draw axes as in question **10** and on them plot points and draw the section.

Is it possible to see P directly from Q?

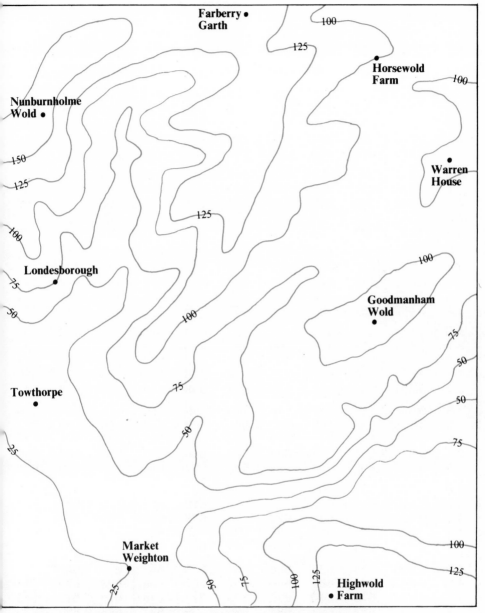

This map shows part of the Yorkshire Wolds with contours at 25 metre intervals.

Construct the five sections described below. For each one, say if one point can be seen from the other point. The heights of each point are given.

 (i) From Market Weighton (25 m) to Warren House (110 m)
 (ii) From Market Weighton (25 m) to Nunburnholme Wold (160 m)
 (iii) From Towthorpe (30 m) to Horsewold Farm (100 m)
 (iv) From Highwold Farm (130 m) to Farberry Garth (140 m)
 (v) From Londesborough (75 m) to Goodmanham Wold (110 m)

Logarithms

	0	1	2	3	4	5	6	7	8	9
1.0	0.000	004	009	013	017	021	025	029	033	037
1.1	0.041	045	049	053	057	061	064	068	072	076
1.2	0.079	083	086	090	093	097	100	104	107	111
1.3	0.114	117	121	124	127	130	134	137	140	143
1.4	0.146	149	152	155	158	161	164	167	170	173
1.5	0.176	179	182	185	188	190	193	196	199	201
1.6	0.204	207	210	212	215	217	220	223	225	228
1.7	0.230	233	236	238	241	243	246	248	250	253
1.8	0.255	258	260	262	265	267	270	272	274	276
1.9	0.279	281	283	286	288	290	292	294	297	299
2.0	0.301	303	305	307	310	312	314	316	318	320
2.1	0.322	324	326	328	330	332	334	336	338	340
2.2	0.342	344	346	348	350	352	354	356	358	360
2.3	0.362	364	365	367	369	371	373	375	377	378
2.4	0.380	382	384	386	387	389	391	393	394	396
2.5	0.398	400	401	403	405	407	408	410	412	413
2.6	0.415	417	418	420	422	423	425	427	428	430
2.7	0.431	433	435	436	438	439	441	442	444	446
2.8	0.447	449	450	452	453	455	456	458	459	461
2.9	0.462	464	465	467	468	470	471	473	474	476
3.0	0.477	479	480	481	483	484	486	487	489	490
3.1	0.491	493	494	496	497	498	500	501	502	504
3.2	0.505	507	508	509	511	512	513	515	516	517
3.3	0.519	520	521	522	524	525	526	528	529	530
3.4	0.531	533	534	535	537	538	539	540	542	543
3.5	0.544	545	547	548	549	550	551	553	554	555
3.6	0.556	558	559	560	561	562	563	565	566	567
3.7	0.568	569	571	572	573	574	575	576	577	579
3.8	0.580	581	582	583	584	585	587	588	589	590
3.9	0.591	592	593	594	595	597	598	599	600	601
4.0	0.602	603	604	605	606	607	609	610	611	612
4.1	0.613	614	615	616	617	618	619	620	621	622
4.2	0.623	624	625	626	627	628	629	630	631	632
4.3	0.633	634	635	636	637	638	639	640	641	642
4.4	0.643	644	645	646	647	648	649	650	651	652
4.5	0.653	654	655	656	657	658	659	660	661	662
4.6	0.663	664	665	666	667	667	668	669	670	671
4.7	0.672	673	674	675	676	677	678	679	679	680
4.8	0.681	682	683	684	685	686	687	688	688	689
4.9	0.690	691	692	693	694	695	695	696	697	698
5.0	0.699	700	701	702	702	703	704	705	706	707
5.1	0.708	708	709	710	711	712	713	713	714	715
5.2	0.716	717	718	719	719	720	721	722	723	723
5.3	0.724	725	726	727	728	728	729	730	731	732
5.4	0.732	733	734	735	736	736	737	738	739	740

	0	1	2	3	4	5	6	7	8	9
5.5	0.740	741	742	743	744	744	745	746	747	747
5.6	0.748	749	750	751	751	752	753	754	754	755
5.7	0.756	757	757	758	759	760	760	761	762	763
5.8	0.763	764	765	766	766	767	768	769	769	770
5.9	0.771	772	772	773	774	775	775	776	777	777
6.0	0.778	779	780	780	781	782	782	783	784	785
6.1	0.785	786	787	787	788	789	790	790	791	792
6.2	0.792	793	794	794	795	796	797	797	798	799
6.3	0.799	800	801	801	802	803	803	804	805	806
6.4	0.806	807	808	808	809	810	810	811	812	812
6.5	0.813	814	814	815	816	816	817	818	818	819
6.6	0.820	820	821	822	822	823	823	824	825	825
6.7	0.826	827	827	828	829	829	830	831	831	832
6.8	0.833	833	834	834	835	836	836	837	838	838
6.9	0.839	839	840	841	841	842	843	843	844	844
7.0	0.845	846	846	847	848	848	849	849	850	851
7.1	0.851	852	852	853	854	854	855	856	856	857
7.2	0.857	858	859	859	860	860	861	862	862	863
7.3	0.863	864	865	865	866	866	867	867	868	869
7.4	0.869	870	870	871	872	872	873	873	874	874
7.5	0.875	876	876	877	877	878	879	879	880	880
7.6	0.881	881	882	883	883	884	884	885	885	886
7.7	0.886	887	888	888	889	889	890	890	891	892
7.8	0.892	893	893	894	894	895	895	896	897	897
7.9	0.898	898	899	899	900	900	901	901	902	903
8.0	0.903	904	904	905	905	906	906	907	907	908
8.1	0.908	909	910	910	911	911	912	912	913	913
8.2	0.914	914	915	915	916	916	917	918	918	919
8.3	0.919	920	920	921	921	922	922	923	923	924
8.4	0.924	925	925	926	926	927	927	928	928	929
8.5	0.929	930	930	931	931	932	932	933	933	934
8.6	0.934	935	936	936	937	937	938	938	939	939
8.7	0.940	940	941	941	942	942	943	943	943	944
8.8	0.944	945	945	946	946	947	947	948	948	949
8.9	0.949	950	950	951	951	952	952	953	953	954
9.0	0.954	955	955	956	956	957	957	958	958	959
9.1	0.959	960	960	960	961	961	962	962	963	963
9.2	0.964	964	965	965	966	966	967	967	968	968
9.3	0.968	969	969	970	970	971	971	972	972	973
9.4	0.973	974	974	975	975	975	976	976	977	977
9.5	0.978	978	979	979	980	980	980	981	981	982
9.6	0.982	983	983	984	984	985	985	985	986	986
9.7	0.987	987	988	988	989	989	989	990	990	991
9.8	0.991	992	992	993	993	993	994	994	995	995
9.9	0.996	996	997	997	997	998	998	999	999	1.000
10.0	1.000									

Squares

	0	1	2	3	4	5	6	7	8	9
1.0	1.00	1.02	1.04	1.06	1.08	1.10	1.12	1.14	1.17	1.19
1.1	1.21	1.23	1.25	1.28	1.30	1.32	1.35	1.37	1.39	1.42
1.2	1.44	1.46	1.49	1.51	1.54	1.56	1.59	1.61	1.64	1.66
1.3	1.69	1.72	1.74	1.77	1.80	1.82	1.85	1.88	1.90	1.93
1.4	1.96	1.99	2.02	2.04	2.07	2.10	2.13	2.16	2.19	2.22
1.5	2.25	2.28	2.31	2.34	2.37	2.40	2.43	2.46	2.50	2.53
1.6	2.56	2.59	2.62	2.66	2.69	2.72	2.76	2.79	2.82	2.86
1.7	2.89	2.92	2.96	2.99	3.03	3.06	3.10	3.13	3.17	3.20
1.8	3.24	3.28	3.31	3.35	3.39	3.42	3.46	3.50	3.53	3.57
1.9	3.61	3.65	3.69	3.72	3.76	3.80	3.84	3.88	3.92	3.96
2.0	4.00	4.04	4.08	4.12	4.16	4.20	4.24	4.28	4.33	4.37
2.1	4.41	4.45	4.49	4.54	4.58	4.62	4.67	4.71	4.75	4.80
2.2	4.84	4.88	4.93	4.97	5.02	5.06	5.11	5.15	5.20	5.24
2.3	5.29	5.34	5.38	5.43	5.48	5.52	5.57	5.62	5.66	5.71
2.4	5.76	5.81	5.86	5.90	5.95	6.00	6.05	6.10	6.15	6.20
2.5	6.25	6.30	6.35	6.40	6.45	6.50	6.55	6.60	6.66	6.71
2.6	6.76	6.81	6.86	6.92	6.97	7.02	7.08	7.13	7.18	7.24
2.7	7.29	7.34	7.40	7.45	7.51	7.56	7.62	7.67	7.73	7.78
2.8	7.84	7.90	7.95	8.01	8.07	8.12	8.18	8.24	8.29	8.35
2.9	8.41	8.47	8.53	8.58	8.64	8.70	8.76	8.82	8.88	8.94
3.0	9.00	9.06	9.12	9.18	9.24	9.30	9.36	9.42	9.49	9.55
3.1	9.61	9.67	9.73	9.80	9.86	9.92	9.99	10.0	10.1	10.2
3.2	10.2	10.3	10.4	10.4	10.5	10.6	10.6	10.7	10.8	10.8
3.3	10.9	11.0	11.0	11.1	11.2	11.2	11.3	11.4	11.4	11.5
3.4	11.6	11.6	11.7	11.8	11.8	11.9	12.0	12.0	12.1	12.2
3.5	12.3	12.3	12.4	12.5	12.5	12.6	12.7	12.7	12.8	12.9
3.6	13.0	13.0	13.1	13.2	13.2	13.3	13.4	13.5	13.5	13.6
3.7	13.7	13.8	13.8	13.9	14.0	14.1	14.1	14.2	14.3	14.4
3.8	14.4	14.5	14.6	14.7	14.7	14.8	14.9	15.0	15.1	15.1
3.9	15.2	15.3	15.4	15.4	15.5	15.6	15.7	15.8	15.8	15.9
4.0	16.0	16.1	16.2	16.2	16.3	16.4	16.5	16.6	16.6	16.7
4.1	16.8	16.9	17.0	17.1	17.1	17.2	17.3	17.4	17.5	17.6
4.2	17.6	17.7	17.8	17.9	18.0	18.1	18.1	18.2	18.3	18.4
4.3	18.5	18.6	18.7	18.7	18.8	18.9	19.0	19.1	19.2	19.3
4.4	19.4	19.4	19.5	19.6	19.7	19.8	19.9	20.0	20.1	20.2
4.5	20.3	20.3	20.4	20.5	20.6	20.7	20.8	20.9	21.0	21.1
4.6	21.2	21.3	21.3	21.4	21.5	21.6	21.7	21.8	21.9	22.0
4.7	22.1	22.2	22.3	22.4	22.5	22.6	22.7	22.8	22.8	22.9
4.8	23.0	23.1	23.2	23.3	23.4	23.5	23.6	23.7	23.8	23.9
4.9	24.0	24.1	24.2	24.3	24.4	24.5	24.6	24.7	24.8	24.9
5.0	25.0	25.1	25.2	25.3	25.4	25.5	25.6	25.7	25.8	25.9
5.1	26.0	26.1	26.2	26.3	26.4	26.5	26.6	26.7	26.8	26.9
5.2	27.0	27.1	27.2	27.4	27.5	27.6	27.7	27.8	27.9	28.0
5.3	28.1	28.2	28.3	28.4	28.5	28.6	28.7	28.8	28.9	29.1
5.4	29.2	29.3	29.4	29.5	29.6	29.7	29.8	29.9	30.0	30.1

Squares

	0	**1**	**2**	**3**	**4**	**5**	**6**	**7**	**8**	**9**
5.5	30.3	30.4	30.5	30.6	30.7	30.8	30.9	31.0	31.1	31.2
5.6	31.4	31.5	31.6	31.7	31.8	31.9	32.0	32.1	32.3	32.4
5.7	32.5	32.6	32.7	32.8	32.9	33.1	33.2	33.3	33.4	33.5
5.8	33.6	33.8	33.9	34.0	34.1	34.2	34.3	34.5	34.6	34.7
5.9	34.8	34.9	35.0	35.2	35.3	35.4	35.5	35.6	35.8	35.9
6.0	36.0	36.1	36.2	36.4	36.5	36.6	36.7	36.8	37.0	37.1
6.1	37.2	37.3	37.5	37.6	37.7	37.8	37.9	38.1	38.2	38.3
6.2	38.4	38.6	38.7	38.8	38.9	39.1	39.2	39.3	39.4	39.6
6.3	39.7	39.8	39.9	40.1	40.2	40.3	40.4	40.6	40.7	40.8
6.4	41.0	41.1	41.2	41.3	41.5	41.6	41.7	41.9	42.0	42.1
6.5	42.3	42.4	42.5	42.6	42.8	42.9	43.0	43.2	43.3	43.4
6.6	43.6	43.7	43.8	44.0	44.1	44.2	44.4	44.5	44.6	44.8
6.7	44.9	45.0	45.2	45.3	45.4	45.6	45.7	45.8	46.0	46.1
6.8	46.2	46.4	46.5	46.6	46.8	46.9	47.1	47.2	47.3	47.5
6.9	47.6	47.7	47.9	48.0	48.2	48.3	48.4	48.6	48.7	48.9
7.0	49.0	49.1	49.3	49.4	49.6	49.7	49.8	50.0	50.1	50.3
7.1	50.4	50.6	50.7	50.8	51.0	51.1	51.3	51.4	51.6	51.7
7.2	51.8	52.0	52.1	52.3	52.4	52.6	52.7	52.9	53.0	53.1
7.3	53.3	53.4	53.6	53.7	53.9	54.0	54.2	54.3	54.5	54.6
7.4	54.8	54.9	55.1	55.2	55.4	55.5	55.7	55.8	56.0	56.1
7.5	56.3	56.4	56.6	56.7	56.9	57.0	57.2	57.3	57.5	57.6
7.6	57.8	57.9	58.1	58.2	58.4	58.5	58.7	58.8	59.0	59.1
7.7	59.3	59.4	59.6	59.8	59.9	60.1	60.2	60.4	60.5	60.7
7.8	60.8	61.0	61.2	61.3	61.5	61.6	61.8	61.9	62.1	62.3
7.9	62.4	62.6	62.7	62.9	63.0	63.2	63.4	63.5	63.7	63.8
8.0	64.0	64.2	64.3	64.5	64.6	64.8	65.0	65.1	65.3	65.4
8.1	65.6	65.8	65.9	66.1	66.3	66.4	66.6	66.7	66.9	67.1
8.2	67.2	67.4	67.6	67.7	67.9	68.1	68.2	68.4	68.6	68.7
8.3	68.9	69.1	69.2	69.4	69.6	69.7	69.9	70.1	70.2	70.4
8.4	70.6	70.7	70.9	71.1	71.2	71.4	71.6	71.7	71.9	72.1
8.5	72.3	72.4	72.6	72.8	72.9	73.1	73.3	73.4	73.6	73.8
8.6	74.0	74.1	74.3	74.5	74.6	74.8	75.0	75.2	75.3	75.5
8.7	75.7	75.9	76.0	76.2	76.4	76.6	76.7	76.9	77.1	77.3
8.8	77.4	77.6	77.8	78.0	78.1	78.3	78.5	78.7	78.9	79.0
8.9	79.2	79.4	79.6	79.7	79.9	80.1	80.3	80.5	80.6	80.8
9.0	81.0	81.2	81.4	81.5	81.7	81.9	82.1	82.3	82.4	82.6
9.1	82.8	83.0	83.2	83.4	83.5	83.7	83.9	84.1	84.3	84.5
9.2	84.6	84.8	85.0	85.2	85.4	85.6	85.7	85.9	86.1	86.3
9.3	86.5	86.7	86.9	87.0	87.2	87.4	87.6	87.8	88.0	88.2
9.4	88.4	88.5	88.7	88.9	89.1	89.3	89.5	89.7	89.9	90.1
9.5	90.3	90.4	90.6	90.8	91.0	91.2	91.4	91.6	91.8	92.0
9.6	92.2	92.4	92.5	92.7	92.9	93.1	93.3	93.5	93.7	93.9
9.7	94.1	94.3	94.5	94.7	94.9	95.1	95.3	95.5	95.6	95.8
9.8	96.0	96.2	96.4	96.6	96.8	97.0	97.2	97.4	97.6	97.8
9.9	98.0	98.2	98.4	98.6	98.8	99.0	99.2	99.4	99.6	99.8
10.0	100									

	0	1	2	3	4	5	6	7	8	9
1.0	1.00	1.00	1.01	1.01	1.02	1.02	1.03	1.03	1.04	1.04
1.1	1.05	1.05	1.06	1.06	1.07	1.07	1.08	1.08	1.09	1.09
1.2	1.10	1.10	1.10	1.11	1.11	1.12	1.12	1.13	1.13	1.14
1.3	1.14	1.14	1.15	1.15	1.16	1.16	1.17	1.17	1.17	1.18
1.4	1.18	1.19	1.19	1.20	1.20	1.20	1.21	1.21	1.22	1.22
1.5	1.22	1.23	1.23	1.24	1.24	1.24	1.25	1.25	1.26	1.26
1.6	1.26	1.27	1.27	1.28	1.28	1.28	1.29	1.29	1.30	1.30
1.7	1.30	1.31	1.31	1.32	1.32	1.32	1.33	1.33	1.33	1.34
1.8	1.34	1.35	1.35	1.35	1.36	1.36	1.36	1.37	1.37	1.37
1.9	1.38	1.38	1.39	1.39	1.39	1.40	1.40	1.40	1.41	1.41
2.0	1.41	1.42	1.42	1.42	1.43	1.43	1.44	1.44	1.44	1.45
2.1	1.45	1.45	1.46	1.46	1.46	1.47	1.47	1.47	1.48	1.48
2.2	1.48	1.49	1.49	1.49	1.50	1.50	1.50	1.51	1.51	1.51
2.3	1.52	1.52	1.52	1.53	1.53	1.53	1.54	1.54	1.54	1.55
2.4	1.55	1.55	1.56	1.56	1.56	1.57	1.57	1.57	1.57	1.58
2.5	1.58	1.58	1.59	1.59	1.59	1.60	1.60	1.60	1.61	1.61
2.6	1.61	1.62	1.62	1.62	1.62	1.63	1.63	1.63	1.64	1.64
2.7	1.64	1.65	1.65	1.65	1.66	1.66	1.66	1.66	1.67	1.67
2.8	1.67	1.68	1.68	1.68	1.69	1.69	1.69	1.69	1.70	1.70
2.9	1.70	1.71	1.71	1.71	1.71	1.72	1.72	1.72	1.73	1.73
3.0	1.73	1.73	1.74	1.74	1.74	1.75	1.75	1.75	1.75	1.76
3.1	1.76	1.76	1.77	1.77	1.77	1.77	1.78	1.78	1.78	1.79
3.2	1.79	1.79	1.79	1.80	1.80	1.80	1.81	1.81	1.81	1.81
3.3	1.82	1.82	1.82	1.82	1.83	1.83	1.83	1.84	1.84	1.84
3.4	1.84	1.85	1.85	1.85	1.85	1.86	1.86	1.86	1.87	1.87
3.5	1.87	1.87	1.88	1.88	1.88	1.88	1.89	1.89	1.89	1.89
3.6	1.90	1.90	1.90	1.91	1.91	1.91	1.91	1.92	1.92	1.92
3.7	1.92	1.93	1.93	1.93	1.93	1.94	1.94	1.94	1.94	1.95
3.8	1.95	1.95	1.95	1.96	1.96	1.96	1.96	1.97	1.97	1.97
3.9	1.97	1.98	1.98	1.98	1.98	1.99	1.99	1.99	1.99	2.00
4.0	2.00	2.00	2.00	2.01	2.01	2.01	2.01	2.02	2.02	2.02
4.1	2.02	2.03	2.03	2.03	2.03	2.04	2.04	2.04	2.04	2.05
4.2	2.05	2.05	2.05	2.06	2.06	2.06	2.06	2.07	2.07	2.07
4.3	2.07	2.08	2.08	2.08	2.08	2.09	2.09	2.09	2.09	2.10
4.4	2.10	2.10	2.10	2.10	2.11	2.11	2.11	2.11	2.12	2.12
4.5	2.12	2.12	2.13	2.13	2.13	2.13	2.14	2.14	2.14	2.14
4.6	2.14	2.15	2.15	2.15	2.15	2.16	2.16	2.16	2.16	2.17
4.7	2.17	2.17	2.17	2.17	2.18	2.18	2.18	2.18	2.19	2.19
4.8	2.19	2.19	2.20	2.20	2.20	2.20	2.20	2.21	2.21	2.21
4.9	2.21	2.22	2.22	2.22	2.22	2.22	2.23	2.23	2.23	2.23
5.0	2.24	2.24	2.24	2.24	2.24	2.25	2.25	2.25	2.25	2.26
5.1	2.26	2.26	2.26	2.26	2.27	2.27	2.27	2.27	2.28	2.28
5.2	2.28	2.28	2.28	2.29	2.29	2.29	2.29	2.30	2.30	2.30
5.3	2.30	2.30	2.31	2.31	2.31	2.31	2.32	2.32	2.32	2.32
5.4	2.32	2.33	2.33	2.33	2.33	2.33	2.34	2.34	2.34	2.34
5.5	2.35	2.35	2.35	2.35	2.36	2.36	2.36	2.36	2.36	2.36
5.6	2.37	2.37	2.37	2.37	2.37	2.38	2.38	2.38	2.38	2.39
5.7	2.39	2.39	2.39	2.39	2.40	2.40	2.40	2.40	2.40	2.41
5.8	2.41	2.41	2.41	2.41	2.42	2.42	2.42	2.42	2.42	2.43
5.9	2.43	2.43	2.43	2.44	2.44	2.44	2.44	2.44	2.45	2.45
6.0	2.45	2.45	2.45	2.46	2.46	2.46	2.46	2.46	2.47	2.47
6.1	2.47	2.47	2.47	2.48	2.48	2.48	2.48	2.48	2.49	2.49
6.2	2.49	2.49	2.49	2.50	2.50	2.50	2.50	2.50	2.51	2.51
6.3	2.51	2.51	2.51	2.52	2.52	2.52	2.52	2.52	2.53	2.53
6.4	2.53	2.53	2.53	2.54	2.54	2.54	2.54	2.54	2.55	2.55
6.5	2.55	2.55	2.55	2.56	2.56	2.56	2.56	2.56	2.57	2.57
6.6	2.57	2.57	2.57	2.57	2.58	2.58	2.58	2.58	2.58	2.59
6.7	2.59	2.59	2.59	2.59	2.60	2.60	2.60	2.60	2.60	2.61
6.8	2.61	2.61	2.61	2.61	2.62	2.62	2.62	2.62	2.62	2.62
6.9	2.63	2.63	2.63	2.63	2.63	2.64	2.64	2.64	2.64	2.64